Certain manufacturing industries were also directly related to mining and quarrying, such as explosives and safety fuses, while foundries and engineering works manufactured mining equipment from giant beam engines to waterwheels or compressed air drills. There were the world-famous firms of Harveys at Hayle or Holmans at Camborne, but there were many local foundries producing agricultural machinery and numerous miscellaneous items.

More traditional manufacturing industries included brewing, malting, paper making, textiles, tanneries and corn milling. The brewery at St Austell has a centre open to visitors. The preserved corn mill at Cotehele is one example that is open to the public. Less conventional mills were powered by the tide, using dams on creeks and estuaries. There were also some tower windmills in Cornwall. Water, however, remained dominant and wheels were also harnessed to work many other industries, particularly in mining.

Transport in the form of roads, canals, railways and ports played a vital role in the industrial development of Cornwall. Although there are good medieval bridges, the notoriously poor roads were not improved until the eighteenth century when turnpike trusts were established to support trade and the mining industries.

Statue of Richard Trevithick outside the library at Camborne

Cornwall was the most westerly outpost of canals in England, most notably at Bude and from Looe to Liskeard. The former was opened to benefit agriculture and had inclined planes instead of locks. The latter carried so much traffic from mines and quarries that it was replaced by a railway. The first Cornish railways or tramways connected mines to ports, first around the Camborne-Redruth district and then around Par, Liskeard and finally Calstock. The Bodmin & Wadebridge Railway of 1834 was the first true steam railway. Tall viaducts are a feature of the main Cornwall Railway (later, GWR) which opened in 1859 when the Saltash Bridge brought a direct connection with the rest of England, to the benefit of trade and the potential tourist industry. Maritime industries include commercial and fishing ports, famous lighthouses, lifeboats and ferries across the wider rivers.

Workers' houses were as important as the industries themselves and the mining and china clay districts have good examples of villages and terraced streets of industrial housing. Such communities were seldom without non-conformist chapels and sometimes institutes, libraries or monuments. Gas and electricity utilities provided the necessities of power and light for the larger towns.

Communications with the rest of the world have a special place in Cornwall, which has been the landfall for undersea cables since the nineteenth century and, later, the site of early wireless transmissions by Marconi. Military works constructed within the industrial period range from Victorian coastal fortifications to Second World War airfields.

Throughout the industrial revolution Cornish engineers and inventors were household names in the world of engineering most especially in relation to mining. Richard Trevithick (1771-1833), the 'Cornish Giant', was the greatest of them all, inventing high pressure steam engines, a road locomotive and the world's first successful railway locomotive. A

3

number of other engineers, such as Arthur Woolf (1766-1837), followed his lead and made their name by designing Cornish beam engines. There were also men like Sir Humphry Davy (1778-1829) of Penzance, scientist and inventor of the coal miner's safety lamp, Sir Goldsworthy Gurney (1793-1875), scientist and inventor of a steam road coach and the Bude light, Henry Trengrouse (1772-1854) of Helston, inventor of the rocket life-saving apparatus, and Davies Gilbert (1767-1839) of St Erth, scientist and adviser to Trevithick and Davy. Scottish-born William Murdock (1754-1839) invented gas lighting at Redruth, while Devonian William Bickford (1774-1834) invented the safety fuse which was manufactured in the heart of the mining district at Tuckingmill near Camborne. Many technological advances were pioneered with the support of engineering dynasties such as the Harvey family of Hayle and the Holmans of Camborne.

Joseph T. Treffry (1782-1850) of Fowey was perhaps Cornwall's greatest industrialist and his wide range of interests reflected the energy of the age. He built Par harbour, a lead smelting works, a canal and tramway to his rich Fowey Consols copper mine, which was powered by numerous waterwheels and one of the finest beam engines of its day, and there were also the Carmears incline, Treffry viaduct, granite quarries at Luxulyan, a second tramway, Newquay harbour and a fleet of sailing ships. In addition, Treffry was an influential chairman of the Cornwall Railway.

The heritage of Cornwall's industry has been guarded by a number of bodies. The Cornish Engine Preservation Society was formed in the 1930s, later combining with the Cornish Waterwheels Preservation Society to become the Trevithick Society which has published newsletters and an annual journal since 1973. Its members have been active in many fields, such as the 'greasy gang' who have restored the Levant beam engine to steam and others who have built a working replica of Trevithick's first road locomotive. In recent years the Trevithick Trust, a separate body, oversaw the preservation and display of a wide range of sites from tin mining to lighthouses and overseas communications. The National Trust has found itself the owner of an equally wide range of industrial monuments, from the Cornish beam engines at East Pool and Levant inherited from the CEPS, to engine houses, mills and wartime coastal defences. Private firms have also preserved industrial artefacts and lastly, many Cornish museums contain collections of industrial interest.

Advert, Launceston mineral water factory, 1897

St Austell Brewery

BREWERIES

Brewing is an age-old activity, undertaken in small local brewhouses until industrial-sized breweries became a feature of the nineteenth century. The 12 Cornish breweries listed in the 1850s had increased to 20 by 1897. Some of these were pub brewhouses but the main breweries included those at Redruth and St Austell, D. Venning & Co.'s Cornwall steam brewery at Liskeard, W.C. Wickett's Treluswell steam brewery at Penryn, with others at Albaston (E. Bowhay & Bros), Falmouth (W. & E.C. Carne) and Hayle (Christopher Ellis & Son). By the 1920s there were just two Cornish breweries, at Redruth and St Austell, and their respective pub signs became a familiar sight around the county.

The Redruth brewery was established by Magor Davey & Co. in about 1742. Having acquired other breweries, such as Carnes of Falmouth, the brewery was itself taken over by Devenish & Co. of Weymouth in the 1930s. In more recent years it passed through different ownerships but was closed in 2004. The St Austell brewery was founded in 1851 by Walter Hicks who started in business as a maltster before building a 'steam brewery' in the Market Square in 1867. His business flourished at a time when the town was expanding and success led to the building of a completely new brewery on the present site in Trevarthian Road in 1893. The St Austell Brewery Co. Ltd was formed in 1934 at the same time that Christopher Ellis & Son's Hayle steam brewery was acquired with 30 pubs.

Some brewery sites included their own malthouses (the Hayle brewery's malthouse later became a furniture store), while there were also separate maltings. Those at Tresillian near Truro belonged to Carnes of Falmouth and made use of water transport. Edward Bowhay & Brothers also had maltings at Albaston near Calstock until the 1920s. The Blue Anchor Inn in Coinagehall Street, Helston, continues to brew its own beer on the premises in an age-old tradition, but today there are several other micro-breweries.

In the late nineteenth century, aerated mineral water was another part of the larger brewers' activities but there were other independent factories in the county. In 1897 the factory at Launceston listed among its products soda, potass, lythia and seltzer waters, sold in siphons or patent bottles. Lemonade, gingerade, ginger ale, ginger draught, orange champagne, Guinness Stout, bottled cider and bottled Bass ales were also available.

1 ST AUSTELL BREWERY
SX 017528
+

Stone and brick brewery buildings designed by Inskipp & Mackenzine, noted brewery architects of London, and erected in 1893-4 off Trevarthian Road (then called Tregonissey Lane). The tall tower dominates the skyline above the town. A visitor centre was opened in 1992 and brewery tours can be arranged. Walter Hicks's firm became the St Austell Brewery Co. Ltd in 1934.

2 REDRUTH BREWERY
SW 695422

Cornwall's oldest brewery complex, dating from 1742. It became Devenish & Co. in the 1930s, but after changes of ownership in more recent years, it closed in 2004. The brewery's horizontal steam engine, manufactured by the Redruth Foundry Co. is said to have been the last engine to work in steam in Cornwall.

Maltings at Tresillian

3 TRESILLIAN MALTINGS
SW 863460

The maltings have long since converted to housing but the kiln is still recognisable beside the A390 through the village. Barley grain was brought up the river in barges at high tide to be offloaded at the quay.

4 LAUNCESTON MINERAL WATER FACTORY
SX 332846

The tall building of the Devon & Cornwall Steam Mineral Water Manufactory stands across the ditch below the castle, from where it is best viewed. It has since been converted, but high up on the wall the logo survives, showing torpedo-shaped bottles associated with aerated mineral waters. Established in 1825 and formerly owned by J.S. Eyre & Co, the works was operated by Geake Brothers in 1897 who advertised: 'The waters of this establishment have been justly esteemed for their purity and excellence for over half a century.'

Mineral water factory, Launceston 1976

Carkeet Brickworks 1986

BRICKWORKS

Despite the wealth of building stones available, from granite to slate, it is perhaps surprising that bricks were also manufactured in Cornwall. Sometimes even the smallest outcrops of clay were exploited if they were found to be suitable. For example, there was even a small brick and pipeworks at the Lizard in 1851. Inferior china clays, discoloured by mineral staining, were also dug and mixed with sand especially for firebricks which were in demand for furnaces and steam engine boilers, while tiles were made for the floors of china clay pan-kilns; other products were even exported. One of the largest producers was the St Day Fire Brick & Clay Co., worked from c1860 until 1912 using a poor quality china clay which was fired in a large circular Hoffman kiln (a type with multiple chambers which allowed for a continuous sequence of firing) and two downdraught beehive kilns. There were brickworks around the china clay district, such as the Carbis Brick & Tile Works near Bugle, Wheal Remfrey near Indian Queens and at Par harbour.

The Gunnislake and Hingston Down area in the extreme east of Cornwall witnessed a 30-year boom from the 1870s when a decomposed elvan stone was exploited for making firebricks, building bricks, paving tiles and terracotta wares. The Tamar Firebrick & Clay Co. (later, Tamar Brickworks & Potteries Ltd) of 1873 had a large works covering 4.5 acres and could produce 80,000 firebricks a week. Brickmaking continued until the mid-1930s. A large circular Hoffman kiln with 16 chambers had a single chimney stack 150 feet [46m] high, long since demolished. The Phoenix Vitrified Paving & Firebrick Works was established in 1874 and although bricks and tiles were exported to Russia's Cronstadt naval base from Calstock Quay, the business had closed by 1890. The Plymouth Works of the Dimson Fire Clay Co. also had a large circular Hoffman kiln and was served by a siding descending from the East Cornwall Mineral Railway. The Calstock Firebrick Co. and Thomas Westlake (later, Hill Westlake & Co.) were also in the area.

More brickworks at Millbrook beside the lower Tamar had a ready market across the estuary in Plymouth. The Devonshire Brick Co.'s works began in the 1880s and continued until about 1935. The clay was dug in a nearby pit and transported by tramway to the works. The Foss Brickworks operated during the same period, and a brickworks at Southdown closed in 1942. All three last worked under the name of the Western Counties Brick Co. and Westbrick Products Ltd from 1928.

Brickwork sites are usually poor survivors after closure when they are soon turned over to other uses, but some traces of the larger works do survive, for example, around Hingston Down and at Carbis, while in contrast there are still two small outlying kilns on Bodmin Moor and Tregonning Hill.

5 CARBIS BRICKWORKS
SX 001595

A square brick chimney stack, distinct from the more usual Cornish round stacks, marks the site of the once-busy Carbis Brick & Tile Works which produced refractory bricks and tiles from 1883 until the 1940s. Three round 'beehive' kilns survive here with a square brick chimney stack. The works is just beside Wheal Prosper pan-kiln (site 19) and can be seen from the road.

6 CARKEET BRICKWORKS
SX 219732

This small brickworks operated in about 1900 on the east side of the Fowey valley in the heart of Bodmin Moor, producing bricks impressed with the name 'Liskeard'. A circular downdraught kiln with a decorative stack survive and a drying shed stands nearby.

7 ST DAY FIREBRICK WORKS
SW 727424

Playing fields occupy a levelled depression which marks the site of one of Cornwall's most important firebrick manufactories. Such bricks were used, for example, in the flue for the Cornish boiler which is now in use at Levant Mine.

8 TREGONNING HILL BRICK KILN
SW 605299

A small circular downdraught brick kiln can be seen from Tregonning Hill standing alone in a field near the site of William Argall's clay works and brickworks of the 1870s. Its stone wall supports a broken beehive roof made of brick.

Some Cornish-made bricks

Overgrown kilns at Carbis Brickworks

CANALS

Early canals were projected in Cornwall, notably around the Camborne mining district where the roads down to the ports were in a terrible state thanks to mineral traffic. There were abortive plans for canals from North Downs to Portreath in 1780, Camborne to Hayle in 1801, and the Gwennap mines to Restronguet Creek in 1808. John Rennie was involved in the Polbrook Canal of 1797 from Wadebridge to Dunmere below Bodmin with a short branch to Ruthenbridge for importing coal and exporting minerals, but nothing came of it. Proposed cross-county projects included a canal to link Hayle and Gweek on the Helford, surveyed by Robert Fulton in 1796, and a 13-mile ship canal with a tunnel (!) between Padstow and Fowey, surveyed by Marc Brunel in 1825.

Canals were built despite these failures, although the so-called 'Copperhouse Canal' of 1769 was really part of the shipping facilities in the port of Hayle. John Edyvean's St Columb Canal was intended to carry sea sand to improve agricultural land. It was begun in 1773 but appears to have only worked for about three years before closing by 1781. There were two separate parts, running inland from Mawgan Porth and St Columb Porth. It was a tub-boat canal, linked to each beach by an inclined plane.

The Bude Canal was the longest tub-boat canal in England, designed by James Green primarily for carrying lime-rich sea sand inland for agricultural purposes. Coal from Wales was also carried, but traffic was always limited. A breakwater and harbour basin with a sea lock were built at Bude and the ambitious canal was opened in 1823-25 and ran for 35 ½ miles [57km] to Druxton near Launceston, with branches into Devon to wharves near Holsworthy. Instead of locks there were six inclined planes to carry the tub-boats along the route, the first two being the longest, at Marhamchurch (836 feet, rising 120 feet and worked by a waterwheel) and Hobbacott Down (935 feet long, rising 225 feet and worked by two buckets in a well, supplemented by a small steam engine). The canal closed in 1891, just seven years before the railway arrived at Bude, although the broader waterway from the basin to Marhamchurch was kept open.

Liskeard & Looe Union Canal - lock below Landlooe Bridge, 1979

John Rennie was involved in 1795 with the Tamar Manure Navigation which was to be a river navigation upstream from Morwellham to Gunnislake and thence a canal past Launceston, with thoughts of joining with the Bude Canal then being proposed. The canal was abandoned but the river was made navigable, with a lock (70 feet by 20 feet) and a straight cut to avoid a fish weir at Nutstakes so that Tamar barges could reach New Bridge by 1801. There was a quay with limekilns where granite and firebricks were later exported and coal was landed for the gasworks. The canalised section of river was navigable until about 1929.

The most successful of the Cornish canals was the 6-mile Liskeard & Looe Union Canal. After many false starts, it was opened in 1828 and ascended the East Looe river valley with 24 locks from Terras Bridge to a basin at Moorswater near Liskeard. Coal and limestone were imported, the latter for limekilns set up beside the canal as far inland as Moorswater. Within a decade rich copper had been discovered at Caradon Hill and the canal was soon carrying increasing tonnages of ores from the mines and granite from Cheesewring Quarry down to the port of Looe. The mineral traffic brought down by the Liskeard & Caradon Railway to Moorswater basin became so great that the company replaced the canal by its own railway all the way to Looe quay in 1860.

The Par Canal also carried minerals when it was opened in 1847, surprisingly late for a canal, as part of Joseph Treffry's industrial enterprise. Just under 2 miles long, it ran from Par harbour to Ponts Mill to connect with the Treffry tramway for carrying copper ores, granite and china clay. Very soon the tramway was continued all the way to the port although the canal continued until 1873.

9 BUDE CANAL
SS 204064
The canal operated 1823-91. At Bude, the canal basin forms a harbour, with a large ship-lock to the sea. The Bude-Stratton Museum is here, with displays in former buildings and smithy of the canal company. A path beside the water of the canal can be followed to Helebridge Wharf (SX 215037) where a workshop contains the last surviving tub-boat of the canal. The Marhamchurch incline is also here (SX 220037) but thereafter the dry canal bed can only be found in traces as far as Crossgate (SX 884342) near Druxton Bridge. The largest incline at Hobbacott Down (SS 243047) is best viewed from a lane across the valley to the south.

10 LISKEARD & LOOE UNION CANAL
SX 249557 to SX 237641
Within a few years of opening in 1828 the canal was carrying thousands of tons of copper ore and granite down the East Looe valley from Moorswater to Looe for shipment. It was replaced by a railway in 1860, although the lower section to Sandplace was used until about 1910. The tidal lock at Terras Bridge survives near a railway level crossing (SX 249557), and most of the other lock sites and some original bridges (e.g. at Landlooe Bridge, SX 250595) can be found along the 6-mile route up the valley to the site of the basins at Moorswater (SX 237641).

11 ST COLUMB CANAL
SX 840626 & SX 870672
Built as two canals in the 1770s, earthworks of this short-lived venture contour along the south side of the valley inland from St Columb Porth past St Columb Minor (SX 840626), and the north side of the north valley (e.g. SX 870672) from Mawgan Porth to near Whitewater, north-west of St Columb Major.

Bude Canal Basin

Rocks Pit Near Bugle, 1979

CHINA CLAY & CHINA STONE

China clay or kaolin derives from the decomposition of feldspar crystals within most granite districts. The properties of kaolin for making fine porcelain were first recognised at Tregonning Hill by William Cookworthy in about 1746. Kaolin has been worked on Bodmin Moor and West Penwith but most extensively within the Hensbarrow or St Austell granite, and the industry has been massively important to the Cornish economy. Today, millions of tons are excavated annually and centuries of working have had a far greater impact on the Cornish landscape than any other quarrying industry, producing huge open pits and the characteristic white conical 'sky-tips' of waste - the 'Cornish Alps'. The clay was first sought for the manufacture of fine pottery, and then also for paper and sizing cotton goods. Today, around 80 per cent is used for filling and coating paper, with some taken by the pharmaceutical, paint and plastics industries.

The history and processes of the industry are shown at the Wheal Martyn china clay museum near St Austell. The traditional way of opening a china clay pit was to remove the overburden before washing the kaolin-bearing material from the face by water diverted via leats from a stream. Traps at the bottom of the pit collected the sandy quartz and unaltered feldspar which was dug out and hauled in self-tipping wagons to the top of a conical 'sky-tip'. The clay slurry was pumped to the surface by waterwheels whenever water was available to turn them, but mostly by beam engines of the type seen on the Cornish mines. Two 50-inch engines are preserved in the St Austell district, at Parkandillick and Goonvean. A 30-inch engine worked at Greensplat until February 1959, the last in Cornwall, and has since been re-erected at the Poldark Mine near Wendron.

At the surface the clay slurry flowed through long 'drags' to deposit the finer sand and mica. It was then thickened to a creamy consistency in settling pits and tanks behind a long pan-kiln or 'dry' where the clay was spread on a tiled floor heated by flues running beneath. The dried clay was stored in the adjacent 'linhay', from which it was loaded into road or rail wagons; the better grades were packed in barrels. Cornwall's largest clay drying complex had a central furnace between two long pan-kilns and was built in 1921 beside the newly-opened Trenance valley branch railway at Trethowel (SW 013536). Clay from John Lovering's Higher and Lower Ninestones pits further up the valley was dried

here before closure. The characteristic long, low pan-kilns with a tall chimney at one end are still features of the clay districts, although large-scale modern methods have taken over.

A network of tramways, railway branches and sidings was developed around Hensbarrow, for transporting the finished clay to the ports of Par, Pentewan and Fowey for shipment elsewhere in the country and abroad. The clay from the Bodmin Moor pits was piped down to pan-kilns next to railway lines at Wenford, Bodmin Road and Moorswater.

Wheal Martyn - settling tanks behind pan kiln

High pressure water jets or monitors have been used in the pits since the early twentieth century. The striking 'Cornish Alps' are now being replaced by massive tips using earth-moving equipment and conveyors, for huge quantities of waste must be disposed of to win just one ton of fine clay. The finest material left over after refining, formerly discharged into rivers, is now collected in residue lagoons. The amalgamations of clay firms after 1919 finally led to the industry becoming dominated by ECC International, now Imerys plc.

A partly kaolinised form of granite known as china stone was quarried as a building material in the past, but its greatest use has been for quality porcelain, as a glaze or in the body of pottery since its discovery at Tregonning Hill in the 1740s. However, the main quarries were developed around Nanpean and St Stephen to the west of St Austell. While the potters ground the higher grades of china stone themselves, the rest was ground locally in mills located in the valleys below the quarries, the best known being at Tregargus. The stone was ground in water-filled pans by rotating arms turned by a waterwheel and the resulting slurry was settled and dried in pan-kilns similar to those used for china clay. Large china stone mills at Ponts Mill near St Blazey were worked by turbines until the 1960s.

12 GLYNN VALLEY CLAY WORKS
SX 143718
China clay was extracted here on Bodmin Moor from 1875 until 1942. Largely untouched since closure, there are sky-tips, a large wheelpit (for pumping and winding), mica drags, settling pits and the remains of a pan-kiln and its chimney. From 1919, clay slurry was piped to a pan-kiln on the railway at Bodmin Road. The more visible but less complete Hawkstor clay pit (SX 150745) is next to the A30 and the remains of other clay pits are at Temple (SX 136732) and Durfold (SX 119738).

Glynn Valley clay works on Bodmin Moor

13 PARKANDILLACK ENGINE
SW 948568
A 50-inch Cornish beam engine made by the Copperhouse Foundry at Hayle in 1852 is preserved in its engine house with boiler alongside. The engine is open and powered by compressed air on occasions by members the Trevithick Society, courtesy of Imerys plc. There is a second engine of the same size at nearby Goonvean (SW 949552), but it is not accessible. It was made by Harvey & Co. of Hayle in 1863 and first worked at three mines around St Agnes before coming here in 1910 to work until 1955.

14 PENDERLEATH CLAY WORKS
SW 498378
The chimney and adjacent pan-kiln at Penderleath mark the site of the clayworks near Towadnack, St Ives. The pit, a short distance to the west, worked in 1922-30 and in its later years the clay slurry was piped to a more convenient drying kiln near the railway at St Erth.

15 TREGARGUS CHINA STONE MILLS
SW 949540
There were once five china stone mills close together in the valley near St Stephen, each worked by a large waterwheel. One survives with its wheel, although in a poor state.

16 TREGONNING HILL PITS
SW 602297
It was somewhere on or around Tregonning Hill that William Cookworthy discovered china stone and clay in the 1740s which led to the rise of this great industry. The St Austell district soon became dominant, but Tregonning, for all its fame, was only worked irregularly and on a small scale because of limited deposits. Overgrown pits are seen along the summit of Tregonning Hill.

Wheal Prosper clay dry and Carbis brick kilns in 2004

17 WENFORD DRY
SX 085744
Now closed, these long pan-kilns at Poley's Bridge were built in 1906 for processing clay brought by pipeline from the Stannon Pit on Bodmin Moor. It was placed here on sidings near the terminus of the Bodmin & Wadebridge Railway. A very small clay works which served a clay pit at Durfold near Blisland lies beside the railway course, now the Camel Trail, at Tresarrett or Stump Oak siding (SX 089725).

18 WHEAL MARTYN CHINA CLAY MUSEUM
SX 005554
+
The museum of the china clay industry is an essential place to visit for anyone interested in Cornwall's industrial past. Two waterwheels of 18ft and 35ft diameter are typical of smaller clay pits to work slurry pumps via flat rods or wire cables, thus avoiding the expense of a steam engine. A guided walk follows the refining processes through the mica drags and settling pits to the final settling tanks behind the dry or pan-kiln. Lines of slender granite posts once supported the roof of the linhay or store from which the dried clay was despatched. Wheal Martyn worked from the 1820s until 1931, with the dry continuing until 1969. The museum was established in 1975 in the abandoned buildings and also has displays on other aspects of the industry. A walk through woods brings the visitor to a viewing platform above the modern Wheal Martyn china clay pit, the whole scale overwhelming the older abandoned pits and tips in the neighbourhood.

19 WHEAL PROSPER KILN
SX 001596
This was the last traditional pan-kiln to be fired by coal, owned by the Goonvean & Rostowrack Co. It was served by the former Carbis branch railway siding, since removed. Now closed and under conversion, it can be seen from the road between Bugle and Roche.

Wheal Prosper china clay dry and railway siding near Rosemellyn, 1979

The Marconi Wireless Station, Lizard

COMMUNICATIONS WITH THE WORLD

Visitors to the Lizard can hardly miss the huge dish aerials of the Goonhilly Earth Station, the visible presence of twenty-first century communications technology. This was the place which received the first live transatlantic television signals via the Telstar satellite in July 1962. Cornwall has a much longer history in the global communications industry, for it saw pioneering work in both the fields of submarine cables and wireless transmissions. Submarine telegraph cables were to span the world from a sandy beach and tiny valley at Porthcurno, the first being laid in 1870. In the following year the Direct Spanish Telegraph Co. laid a cable to Housel Bay on the Lizard peninsula, lasting 50 years before it was redirected to Porthcurno. The submarine telegraph cables were highly insulated and protected but, once ashore and having passed through the receiving station, the signals were carried inland by ordinary wires on poles. The Eastern Telegraph Co., which later became Cable & Wireless, developed an important centre at Porthcurno, where a training college was opened alongside the telegraph office. The site now has a fascinating museum.

Cornwall also saw the early days of radio transmission when Guglielmo Marconi experimented at the Lizard. The first over-the-horizon signal was sent from the Isle of Wight to the Lizard on 23 January 1901, but Marconi used the clifftop at Poldhu for the first transatlantic signal in the following December. The Poldhu site, established in 1900, became a wireless telegraphy station until 1933.

20 LIZARD WIRELESS TELEGRAPHY STATION
SW 712119
+

Beside the coast path on Pen Olva near Lizard Point are the original bungalow buildings used by Guglielmo Marconi for receiving the historic first over-the-horizon radio signal from the Isle of Wight, a distance of 186 miles, on 23 January 1901. The event was re-enacted by enthusiasts exactly a century later. The wireless station was later used for communicating with ships for a few years. Replica equipment has been installed at this historic site. The mast footings also survive. Down below, the line of the Direct Spanish Telegraph Co.'s 1871 cable can be seen ascending the cliff in Housel Bay.

21 POLDHU WIRELESS STATION SITE
SW 664194
A monument on the clifftop records the site where the first transatlantic radio transmission (the letter 'S' in Morse code) was made to Marconi listening at Signal Hill, Newfoundland, on 12 December 1901. A circle of twenty 200-foot wooden

masts had been blown down in September, so a simpler aerial sufficed. Soon, the wireless station grew and had four 235-foot tall lattice masts. The Marconi Company used the site for research and communications with Europe and shipping until 1933. Nearby, the Marconi Centre is open to the public courtesy of the Poldhu Amateur Radio Club.

22 PORTHCURNO MUSEUM OF SUBMARINE TELEGRAPHY
SW 384227
+

The Porthcurno station ('PK') was the hub of a telegraph network spanning the world, connected with 14 submarine cables up the beach or nearby cliffs. The first cable to Gibraltar and Lisbon was landed at the beach in 1870 and a second cable to Vigo followed in 1873. Meanwhile the Eastern Telegraph Co. was formed, eventually becoming Cable & Wireless. Cable station buildings and accommodation for its employees were built in the valley. On the east side the block of the Eastern Telegraph Office now houses the museum, while behind are the underground facilities mined from beneath the hill for security in 1940. Well-presented displays of telegraph equipment of all periods explain the importance of this means of communication. A pyramid

The line of the Direct Spanish Telegraph cable in the cliff at Housel Bay, Lizard

on the clifftop of Percella Point to the east marks the site of the 'PQ' hut which received the French cable which crossed the Atlantic via Brest. It was redirected to Porthcurno beach in 1919.

The Eastern Telegraph Office at Porthcurno is now a museum

EXPLOSIVES

Explosives were essential to the working of the Cornish mines, as well as the quarries in later years. Although there was a ready market here, gunpowder had to be imported from outside the county until about 1807 when the first local works opened at Cosawes Wood near Ponsanooth, followed not long afterwards by another at nearby Kennall Vale which became the largest in Cornwall. Remote wooded sites with available water power for working the incorporating mills were favoured at places such as here and at Herodsfoot and Trago Mills in east Cornwall. For raw materials, charcoal could be obtained locally but sulphur and saltpetre or nitre were imported. The remote sites reduced the risks to surrounding inhabitants should there be an accident, while the effect of the trees might also shield some of the blast. The primitive method of firing gunpowder with 'quills' or 'straws' led to increasing numbers of accidents in the mines as the industry expanded in the early nineteenth century. A saviour was found in the invention of the safety fuse by William Bickford in 1831. The manufacturing of safety fuses, especially at Tuckingmill near Camborne, became an important aspect of the explosives industry.

There were various attempts to produce more powerful explosives, but the outstanding success came with Nobel's dynamite. It was later produced in Cornwall at large factories established at Hayle and Perranporth, although by then the Cornish mines were in decline. In 1889 the Kennall Gunpowder Co. branched out and established the National Explosives Co.'s works at Hayle Towans, which made dynamite and other high explosives, including guncotton and cordite for military purposes. An accident here in 1904 caused a major explosion great enough to shatter the east window of St Ives church across the bay. The factory closed in 1920. After 1891 dynamite was manufactured by the British & Colonial Explosives Co. out on the clifftop at Cligga Head near Perranporth. Nobel's Explosives took over in 1893 and continued manufacturing until 1905. The factory closed soon after a revival in the Great War. Trago Mills and the East Cornwall Gunpowder Co.'s works at Herodsfoot produced the quarrying explosive 'Burrowite' from the 1930s until the 1960s.

Abandoned water-powered gearing in an incorporating mill at Kennall Vale

23 HAYLE EXPLOSIVES FACTORY
SW 578397
A chimney stack at Upton Towans marks part of the extensive site of the National Explosive Co.'s factory, established in 1889 to make dynamite. Nitroglycerine, cordite and guncotton were also made in separate buildings scattered among the dunes. A railway branch was laid from Hayle and over 1,800 persons were employed in the Great War. The factory closed in 1920 but the site was retained by ICI until 1973.

24 KENNALL VALE GUNPOWDER MILLS
SW 751375
Started in 1811 by the Fox family, the Kennall Gunpowder Co. eventually passed to the large national firm of Curtis's & Harvey in 1898 and gunpowder making ceased soon after. The gunpowder factory was the most important in Cornwall and was established in the wooded valley, and extended in 1844. The site made common blasting powder for mines and quarries and special powder for safety fuses. The raw materials were ground and 'incorporated' with edge runner stones in a series of mills powered by waterwheels. Watercourses and the walls of the incorporating mills survive, and include a broken iron waterwheel made by Dingey of Truro. This attractive woodland site is a nature reserve, accessed from Ponsanooth village off Park Road and Cot Hill.

25 PERRANPORTH EXPLOSIVES WORKS
SW 742536
Some traces remain at the site of the British & Colonial Explosives Co.'s works, established well clear of habitation on Cligga Head in 1891, but soon taken over by Nobel's Explosives. It had a short life but was revived during the Great War to supply munitions. The site is confused by the presence of mining activity and the Second World War airfield.

26 TUCKINGMILL FUSE FACTORY
SW 660410
A plaque near the bottom of Pendarves Street, Tuckingmill, commemorates the invention of the safety fuse by William Bickford, whose factory was well placed to serve the mines of Camborne, Redruth and beyond. The factory was established after 1831 and worked until 1961. The safety fuse was one of the great inventions to improve the dangerous lot of all miners, premature explosions being one of the main causes of death and injury up to that date. In 1900, around 800 people were employed here and at nearby rival William Bennett's fuse factory. Tuckingmill has been termed the 'fuse making capital of the world'. The buildings, now derelict or given over to other uses, have a granite-arched entrance where the initials 'BS&Co' stand for Bickford, Smith & Co.

FERRIES

There are ancient ferry crossings in south Cornwall, such as at Cremyll (Tamar), Bodinnick (Fowey) and King Harry Passage (Fal). The most important chain ferries or floating bridges for vehicles were opened across the Tamar at Saltash and Torpoint in 1833 and 1834, designed by James Meadows Rendel who was responsible for similar ferries at Dartmouth, Southampton and Gosport. A steam engine on board drew the vessel across the river by means of two chains. The Torpoint ferry was replaced by other steam ferries in 1871 and again in 1926-31 (built by Philip & Son of Dartmouth), before diesel ferries arrived in the 1960s from Thornycroft of Southampton and Charles Hill of Bristol. The last Saltash ferry became disused in 1961 when the new suspension road bridge was opened, but the slipways survive. This steam floating bridge, built by Thornycroft in 1933, was converted to diesel and used for a while as the King Harry Ferry (SW 841396). A more modern ferry now crosses at the latter.

27 TORPOINT FERRY   SX 441551
Although modern diesel-powered floating bridges cross here, the principle has been the same since 1834 with each vessel pulling itself across the Tamar along the guiding chains. The chain balance towers are a notable feature on the shore.

Every cove and harbour around the Cornish coast has associations in some way with the fishing industry, past or present. The heritage of the fishing industry can be seen on the land in the old fish cellars or 'palaces' which were used as stores and for processing pilchards. There are good examples at Polkerris (said to be the largest) on St Austell Bay, and at Port Gaverne and Port Isaac on the north coast, while at Newlyn a pilchard works still operates in the traditional way and can be visited. Pilchard press stones can be found in the fishing ports, set aside or having found a variety of new uses. There are examples at the harbour of St Michael's Mount. The fish cellars, fish markets, net lofts and ice stores all distinguish fishing ports from trading ports. Some traditional-type fishing luggers can be seen under sail around the ports.

28 NEWLYN PILCHARD WORKS
SW 462291
+
The traditional methods of pressing and curing pilchards can be observed by visitors at The Pilchard Works, a working factory and museum in the fishing port of Newlyn. The pilchards are pressed and packed into wooden barrels and have been exported to countries such as Italy since 1905.

29 PORT GAVERNE FISH CELLARS
SX 003808
The Union Cellars and Rashleigh Cellars are two fish cellars or 'palaces' where fishermen processed pilchards and stored and repaired their equipment. Another good example of a fish cellar is on the west side of neighbouring Port Isaac harbour (SW 996808) where fishing boats are still beached.

30 SENNEN COVE ROUNDHOUSE
SW 351263
The sturdily-built roundhouse was a capstan house for hauling fishing boats up the beach at Sennen Cove. The top floor is a gift shop but the timber and iron capstan still survives underneath. A round house at Church Cove (SW 714128) on the Lizard has been converted to a house, while on the south coast of West Penwith, an open capstan has been restored by the National Trust on the beach at Penberth Cove (SW 403227).

Holman Brothers' factory, Camborne

FOUNDERS & ENGINEERS

Harvey & Co. of Hayle was the most famous of all the foundries and engineering works established during the Industrial Revolution. A small foundry was started at Carnsew by John Harvey in 1779 and it grew into a large foundry and engineering works, with the business expanding to include general merchants, ship-owning and ship building. For over a century huge steam engines were cast and built here for the mines in Cornwall and abroad, while much other mining equipment was manufactured and iron ships were also built. Richard Trevithick spent some time here, experimenting and making his high pressure steam engines or 'puffers' and his steam road vehicle in 1801. He married John Harvey's daughter Jane in 1797 at a time when her brother Henry took over the family business. Beam engines were also supplied for waterworks in London and for draining the Severn Tunnel. The largest engine ever built had a cylinder of 144-inches diameter and drained the Haarlemmermeer in Holland from 1849 to 1933. This Cruquius engine has been preserved and is open to visitors today. Around 1,000 were employed at Harvey & Co's height but the foundry side of the business closed in 1903.

The Harveys made full use of the mining port of Hayle, where the company built extensive quays. From the early years there was intense trade rivalry with the Cornish Copper Co. on the east side of town, continuing when it became the Copperhouse Foundry, where Messrs Sandys, Carne & Vivian manufactured large beam engines and many other iron items. Some justice was achieved when the Copperhouse Foundry closed in 1867 and was bought out by Harvey & Co. It is of note that today the Kew Bridge Steam Museum in London has preserved two giant Hayle beam engines from Harvey (100-inch cylinder) and Copperhouse (90-inch). The long-established firm of J. & F. Pool later occupied the old Copperhouse works, specialising in metal perforating.

Meanwhile, the Perran Wharf Foundry was established by the Fox family in 1791. It was not well placed for receiving raw materials or shipping its products, being at the head of a narrow tidal creek upstream from Devoran. Nevertheless, many notable engines were made here too before Williams' Perran Foundry Co. closed in 1879.

The Holmans were a well known Cornish engineering family. Nicholas Holman started

'Perran Foundry 1791' lintel, Perran Foundry

a foundry at Camborne in 1801 but it was not until 1880 that Holman Brothers Engineering was named and their mining equipment and drilling machinery became world famous. Beam engines were also made. The last of the Holman-Compair factories closed in 2003. Meanwhile, Nicholas Holman junior had opened a foundry at St Just in 1834, which finally closed in 1968. The business expanded to Penzance in the 1830s and N. Holman & Sons were engineers and ship-repairers at the drydock in Penzance in the years 1904-95.

William West established a successful foundry at St Blazey in 1848, where large steam engines were among the products. A 22-inch rotative beam engine was designed and made here in 1851 and worked at Rostowrack clay pit for 91 years until 1952. After West's death in 1879 his sons took over until 1891. In the same area were the St Austell Foundry (bought by West in 1856) and the Charlestown Foundry, which was established in 1827 and for many years made equipment for the china clay industry.

There were around 60 foundries in nineteenth-century Cornwall, and not all were making steam engines and equipment for the mines. Cast and wrought iron were used for making edge tools, boilers, agricultural machinery, waterwheels, mill gearing, winches, lintels, bridges, lamp posts, road signs and kitchen ranges known as 'Cornish slabs'.

Edge tools were made at the water-powered Roseworthy Hammer Mill (1790-1939) near Camborne and the Redruth Hammer Mills Foundry was begun by William Sara in 1860. Francis Dingey's Truro Foundry made waterwheels and examples are known at the Kennall Vale gunpowder mills and Blue Hills streamworks in Cornwall, while a splendid wheel survives at a remote copper mine in the Snowdonia mountains. Among the other foundries were Walter Visick & Sons of Devoran, the Roseland Vale Foundry (Menheniot), Dunheved Ironworks (Launceston) and William Brenton's East Cornwall Iron Works established in 1840 at Polbathick, St Germans, where agricultural machinery was made, including seed drills. At Wadebridge, Oatey & Martin Ltd's important foundry worked from 1833 until 1958. G.H. Harris listed waterwheels among his products from 1890 at his Wadebridge foundry which has been occupied as a jobbing foundry by Irons Brothers Ltd since 1925.

Many waterwheels were made by local iron-founders, such as Jabez Buckingham of North Hill, seen cast on the wheel at Trewerry Mill

31 HARVEYS HAYLE FOUNDRY
SW 558371

This important site where many large beam engines were made has been the subject of regeneration in recent years. What is left of the once extensive foundry, and which can be viewed by the public, includes the remains of the hammer mill, ropery, grist mill and millpond. Unfortunately, the impressive range of the fitting shop alongside the Helston road was demolished in 1984, but further buildings are under restoration nearby. A 13-inch Crimean siege mortar weighing 5 tons was made by Harvey & Co. in 1856 and is preserved beside the Penzance road on the western edge of Hayle.

32 HOLMAN BROTHERS FACTORY
SW 649398

Rock drills were manufactured at this site by the famous engineering firm of Holman Brothers from the late nineteenth century onwards. The buildings are close to the railway station at Camborne, alongside Trevu Road, while opposite the Passmore Edwards Library and Trevithick memorial was the Holman industrial museum, alas, long since closed.

33 PERRAN FOUNDRY
SW 776384

The site at Perran Wharf has long been proposed for an industrial museum, but has lain derelict for many years. The buildings, which were later taken over by a milling company, include a cast-iron arch cast with 'Perran Foundry 1791'. The foundry made steam engines and mining equipment and had its own gasworks. There were extensive timber ponds here at the head of the creek and nearby beside

Hayle foundry pond

Holman rock drill rig, displayed at Poldark Mine

the A39 road, the Norway Inn takes its name from the ships which brought timber from Scandinavia.

34 ST BLAZEY FOUNDRY
SX 070546

Some buildings of William West's St Blazey foundry are still recognisable in Station Road, now occupied by builders' merchants. William West designed and built the celebrated 80-inch Austen's engine for Fowey Consols mine in 1834, proved in trials to be extremely efficient. West's grave is in St Blazey churchyard.

Harvey & Co.'s mortar dates from the Crimean War

LIGHT & POWER

The first use of coal gas to light a house is attributed to William Murdock in 1792 when he was living at Redruth (site 127). It was not until the 1830s that Cornish towns began erecting gasworks for lighting streets and households. Cooking and heating were to follow with improved gas mains and by the end of the century there were 25 works in most of the largest towns. Some iron foundries such as at Hayle and Perran Wharf had their own gasworks which could supply the local community. The latter may have had the first gasworks in Cornwall, c1799.

With nationalisation and the laying of a main network, many of the small local gasworks were closed in the 1950s and '60s. Torpoint gasworks was said to be the last hand-fired gas plant in England when it closed in 1967, and the Bude gasworks of 1908 closed in 1970. A gasworks, with its retorts, smells and gas holder, was a familiar if unloved scene in many towns, but the end finally came with the introduction of natural gas.

Once introduced, electricity soon rivalled gas for lighting, heating and power. It was much more convenient and pylons and overhead wires allowed it to be distributed to the remotest places. The first generators were for private supplies and in 1878 Trinity House installed a generating plant for an electric light at the Lizard. Mines erected their own generating plant, such as the Central Power Station of the St Ives Consolidated Mines Ltd in 1908-15, powered by four 200HP diesel engines. Public supplies were not all a success at first. In 1886 Veale & Co. Ltd provided a public supply to St Austell and it is of interest that Mevagissey claims the first public street lighting in Cornwall in 1896.

Edmundsons Electricity Corporation's Urban Electric Supply Co. Ltd supplied Camborne and Redruth from its steam-powered Carn Brea Generating Station at Pool, as well as running the electric tramway. In 1902 the Cornwall Electric Power Co. had plans to supply Dolcoath tin mine at Camborne, and a few years later a power station was begun at Hayle. In time the company supplied much of Cornwall's power. However, Bude had a power station erected in 1902 by Christy Bros. and from 1906 Falmouth had its own electricity works on Beacon Hill, where refuse was among the fuels until it closed in 1951. A hydro-electric generating station at Pontsmill near St Blazey worked until about 1950.

Hayle Power Station (SW 553381) was gradually expanded after 1910, and was connected to the forerunner of the National Grid in 1933. Hot cooling water was diverted from the power station through ICI's British Ethyl Works in 1938 to extract bromide from seawater. The station was run down and closed in the 1970s, the boiler and turbine houses and its twin chimneys being demolished in 1981. The power station had been a well-known landmark on the north side of the estuary, where it was supplied with coal brought by coasters risking the hazards of Hayle Bar.

LIMEKILNS

Apart from very small outcrops near Launceston and Millbrook, there is no limestone in Cornwall and so all materials for limeburning had to be imported by sea: limestone from south Devon, Gower or Pembrokeshire and culm fuel from South Wales. Burnt in a kiln, the lime was used for building mortar but especially by farmers for neutralising the acid Cornish soils. Hence limekilns are found all around the coast wherever a landing could be made and far up just about every creek that could be navigated by a sailing trader. Over 200 limekiln sites are known in Cornwall, and over 160 of these are in and around the estuaries, beaches and creeks of the south coast. Kilns are prominent on branches of the Tamar, Looe, Fowey and Fal estuaries.

The limekiln at Pont Quay, Fowey estuary

There were at least 18 sites on the Cornish bank of the Tamar between Saltash and Gunnislake, representing some 31 limekiln pots. The four kilns at Halton Quay (SX 413655) ceased in 1916 and were the last to burn on the Tamar. Others are well preserved, for example, at Bohetherick, Cotehele and Okel Tor. At Looe, the estuary was only navigable as far as Sandplace, where there were limekilns, but the Liskeard & Looe Canal carried limestone and culm further inland to three banks of kilns at Moorswater. Kilns stand at the back of beaches, for example, at Polkerris, Pentewan and West Portholland. Kilns are less common on the north coast, where lime-rich shelly sand was available; indeed, the Bude Canal was intended to carry this and tramway rails near the canal basin were for trucks carrying sand from the beach. Surviving examples include kilns at Port Gaverne and Boscastle.

A typical limekiln is a rectangular structure built of local stone with an arched tunnel at the front giving access to a draw hole from which lime was extracted from the base of the pot. The circular pot is lined with brick or stone and tapers towards the bottom. Most kilns are free-standing and would have been loaded from the top by means of a ramp. Some kilns have a second draw arch at the side, while a bank of two or more kilns will have arches giving access to the kilns on both sides.

35 BOSCASTLE LIMEKILN
SX 098913
A rare north-coast limekiln stands alongside of the harbour at Boscastle, once part of the busy scene here but now probably little noticed by the many visitors who walk past. There is another limekiln a few miles down the coast at Port Gaverne (SX 003808).

36 COTEHELE QUAY LIMEKILNS
SX 423680
Two banks of large limekilns stand behind the quay at Cotehele, once an important place for shipping ores and importing Plymouth limestone and Welsh culm for burning and distributing the lime to the neighbourhood. One has three round access arches for two pots, alongside a

A bank of limekilns at Moorswater near Liskeard

probable burner's house. The second bank, which may be earlier in date, has three pots accessed through unusual half-arches.

37 FOWEY ESTUARY KILNS
SX 104596 to SX 119511

A well preserved bank of limekilns shows the importance of navigation on the Fowey estuary to its highest tidal point at Lostwithiel (SX 104596). Downstream, kilns at the head of the creek at Lerryn (SX 139569) have half-arches, similar to those at Cotehele Quay. Typical of many creeks on the south Cornish estuaries, Pont Pill (SX 143518) off Fowey harbour was an important local trading place and a well preserved limekiln stands beside the wharf here. Right at the harbour mouth, a limekiln at Readymoney Cove (SX 119511) has been disguised as a shelter behind the beach.

38 MOORSWATER LIMEKILNS
SX 236641

Three banks of limekilns at the head basin of the Liskeard & Looe Canal were ideally placed, far inland where the burnt lime could serve the needs of farmers and builders over a wide area. Only one bank remains on the east side, but a most interesting one is beside the East Looe River, alongside a limeburner's cottage. Although part of the double kiln is damaged, it contains the remains of a waterwheel and winding mechanism which drew wagons of limestone and culm from the canal basin up an incline supported on piers to the top where a turntable directed them to either pot.

39 SANDPLACE LIMEKILNS
SX 248571 & SX 250567

Three banks of limekilns survive around Sandplace at the highest tidal point of the East Looe River. The Liskeard & Looe Canal carried limestone and fuel further up the valley to kilns at St Keyne and Moorswater. There are other limekilns on the West Looe River at Watergate (SX 233550).

40 TIDEFORD LIMEKILNS
SX 349596 & SX 353599

It is hard to believe that sailing barges once came up this branch of the Lynher estuary but, if proof is needed, there are the remains of three banks of limekilns with three pots each. Higher Quay is the best preserved (SX 349596) near the village and the others at Kilna Quay (SX 353599) and Kilna Park are divided by the busy A38.

Military works were built during the industrial period, and indeed on an industrial scale, such as the massive ring of defences erected in the mid-nineteenth century to protect Plymouth and Devonport Dockyard, including forts on the Cornish side of the Tamar. Lesser gun batteries of this period can be seen at St Catherine's Castle at Fowey or The Island at St Ives, and there are also late Victorian coastal batteries. Mass-concrete gun emplacements, lookouts and searchlight positions were built during both the world wars along the coast, particularly around the approaches to Devonport and Falmouth. Coastal defensive pill-boxes are found at many locations, as varied as one atop the old limekiln at Polkerris and another used by a sailing club at Pentewan.

An airship station was established at Mullion during the Great War, but great advances in aircraft development had been made before the following conflict. RAF airfields and naval air stations for fighters and bombers were constructed during the Second World War on coastal plateau sites at St Eval (1939), St Merryn (1940), Perranporth (1941), Portreath (1941), Predannack (1941), St Mawgan (1943) and Culdrose (1944), while inland was Davidstow (1942). Grass field operations took place at St Just, Treligga (a gunnery and bombing range) and Cleave. Runways, control towers, dispersals, blast pens, bunkers and a miscellany of buildings survive at many sites.

41 DAVIDSTOW AIRFIELD
SX 150850

A lane crosses the bleak, flat Davidstow Moor which has the obvious remains of the wartime airfield of 1942-45. American bombers left here to attack U-boat pens at St Nazaire in Operation Torch in late 1942 and subsequent activities included air-sea rescue and anti-submarine patrols. Although part has been forested, most of the runways and dispersals are intact, with bunkers and a few buildings around the perimeter (some part of a milk factory). The empty control tower is the most poignant reminder of the busy periods of take-off and landing when the airfield was not shrouded in low cloud - not surprising as this was the highest in Britain, at 970 feet above sea level.

42 PENDENNIS CASTLE
SW 825317
+

Henry VIII's castle (English Heritage) is surrounded by gun emplacements of later periods, including the nineteenth and twentieth century. Falmouth docks were of strategic importance during both world wars and down towards the headland are searchlight positions and an observation post. The defences are complemented by others added to St Mawes Castle and St Anthony Head (site 44) across the water.

43 PERRANPORTH AIRFIELD
SW 740528

The clifftop airfield operated in 1941-46 and all the original fighter pens survive with a number of other features. Parts are

The distinctive control tower on the bleak airfield site at Davidstow Moor

Mid-nineteenth century gun emplacements at Pendennis Castle

The Island Battery at St Ives, with the coastguard lookout erected on one of the granite gun emplacements.

not to be confused with the remains of the explosives works on Cligga Head.

44 PLYMOUTH DEFENCES

On the Cornish side of the Tamar estuary and Plymouth Sound there are Victorian forts at Cawsand (SX 433503), Picklecombe (SX 456515) and Scraesdon (SX 393549), while Polhawn (SX 421492) and Tregantle (SX 387533) command Whitsand Bay. This defensive line encircling Plymouth and Devonport Dockyard becomes apparent when the forts are identified with those in Devon on an Ordnance Survey map. Supplies were once brought to the Scraesdon and Tregantle forts by a military railway from Wacker Quay (SX 389551) on the Lynher River estuary, where a corrugated iron engine shed survives. Most of the forts can be viewed from a distance, and there are smaller batteries and defensive positions of later periods out towards Rame Head.

45 ST ANTHONY HEAD BATTERY

SW 847312

Gun batteries at St Anthony Head defended Falmouth's harbour entrance from the nineteenth century until 1956. A battery was built in 1885 behind a rock-cut ditch, and the defences were enlarged in 1904 with two 6-inch guns and an underground magazine. A battery observation post of the Second World War and former searchlight positions are also preserved here by the National Trust.

This pill-box on the beach at Polkerris supports a sailing club building

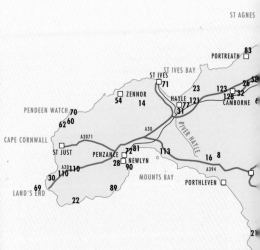

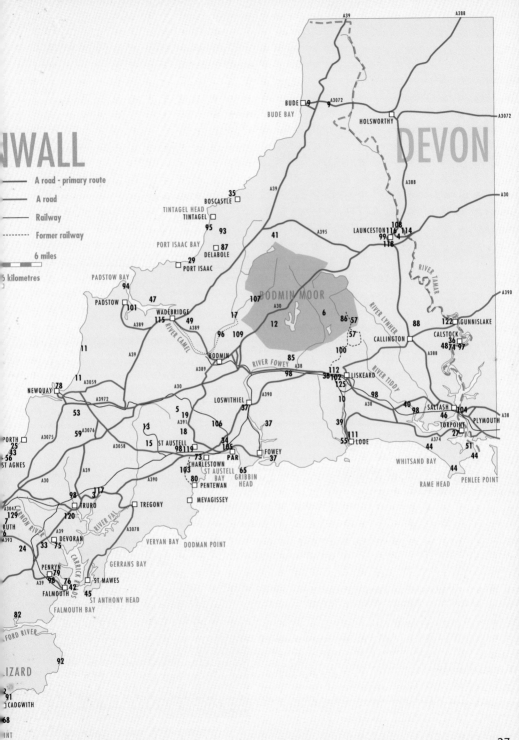

NWALL

- A road - primary route
- A road
- Railway
- Former railway

6 miles

6 kilometres

DEVON

BUDE 9 A3072
BUDE BAY
HOLSWORTHY

A39

A3072

A388

A3072

A388

A39

BOSCASTLE 35
TINTAGEL HEAD
TINTAGEL

A39

A395
LAUNCESTON 116
99 4 114
118 108

PORT ISAAC BAY
DELABOLE 87
29 PORT ISAAC

95 93

41

RIVER TAMAR

PADSTOW BAY
PADSTOW 101
47

94

107

BODMIN MOOR

12

86 57
57

RIVER LYNHER

88

GUNNISLAKE 122
CALSTOCK
4874 97
36

6

WADEBRIDGE
115 49
RIVER CAMEL
A389
96 109
17

A389

A30

100

CALLINGTON

A388

11

A39

BODMIN

A389

RIVER FOWEY

85

A38
98

112
30 102
125

LISKEARD

RIVER TIDDY

10

98

11 A3059
NEWQUAY 78

A3972

LOSWITHIEL

A390

37

A30

40
98 SALTASH 104
46

PLYMOUTH

A38

53

5 19

A391

18

106

37

39

55 111

TORPOINT
27

A38

59 A3076

13

15 ST AUSTELL

98119

34
105

73

PAR
37

FOWEY
37

LOOE

44

51

44

44

A374

A3075

A3058

CHARLESTOWN
ST AUSTELL
BAY
65
GRIBBIN
HEAD

WHITSAND BAY

RAME HEAD

PENLEE POINT

ORTH
25
43
56
ST AGNES

A39

103
80 PENTEWAN

MEVAGISSEY

A30

A390

98 7 17
3

TRURO
120

TREGONY

RIVER FAL

A3047
129
RUTH
6
A393

24

33 75

DEVORAN

A39

A3078

VERYAN BAY

DODMAN POINT

GERRANS BAY

PENRYN
79
98 76
42
FALMOUTH
45
ST ANTHONY HEAD

ST MAWES

CARRICK ROADS

A39

FALMOUTH BAY

82

FORD RIVER

92

LIZARD

2
91
CADGWITH

68

INT

27

Loggans Mill at Hayle, an impressive ruin

Cornwall's abundant fast-flowing streams have powered water mills for grinding corn and other applications. There are many mill sites, often tucked away in hidden valleys or on farms, and there must have been many more as a glance at any early Ordnance Survey map will show. There were some interesting sites, such as at Ridgegrove Mills near Launceston, which had corn and bone mills alongside. Most of the mills were small and have often been converted to housing, but some remain with machinery and perhaps a wheel too.

In the twentieth century, mills closed or were adapted to meet competition, by installing gas or oil engines and even replacing the traditional stones with roller-mills (such was the case at Gweek, for example). Other large mills were purpose-built to employ steam power, such as Loggans Mill, Hayle. This large structure on the eastern fringe of the town has long been derelict and awaits redevelopment. Water-milling on a regular basis ceased in the 1960s, although Cotehele Mill has been restored to a working condition today. Lower Gweek Mills were converted to flats in the late 1970s. Until then the mill retained its machinery and two large waterwheels in tandem on the west side, one of 25 feet diameter, made by Redruth Iron Foundry, and the other 33 feet diameter, made by Holmans of Penzance and St Just. The mill, at the very head of the tidal Helford River, used barges to bring in grain and take away flour, while also serving the local farmers and merchants.

A number of farms utilised water power for working machinery in barns, such as millstones, animal feed machinery, threshers, sawmills, water pumps and even a bone crusher. Sometimes rotary shafting of some length was required to connect between the waterwheel site and the barn.

Of special interest are the unusual watermills known as tidemills that once operated on about a dozen creeks on the Cornish estuaries. High tide filled an artificial pool behind a dam across a suitable creek so that the water was then used to power the mill wheels as the tide receded. Around the lower Tamar estuary there is a good example at Antony Passage on the Lynher, and the sites of others between Antony and Sheviock and at St John's Lake and Millbrook Lake. West Looe has a tidemill and pool. On the north coast, there was a tidemill at the head of the Copperhouse creek at Hayle and another on Little Petherick Creek off the Camel estuary near Padstow.

Cornwall is a naturally windswept county and there are over 60 known windmill sites from Maker in the east to the Lizard in the south. Post-mills were first recorded in the twelfth century but the few remains are of stone tower mills, erected from the late sixteenth century onwards. The old Fowey windmill tower became a folly in the grounds of Fowey Hall, while a tower above Trevone just west of Padstow was later used to support a water tank (SW 897749).

Trewerry Mill, Trerice/St Newlyn East

Antony Passage tide mill vewed from Forder viaduct

46 ANTONY PASSAGE TIDEMILL
SX 414575

Antony Passage Mill was in use until the 1880s. It had four wheels, served by a large mill pool. There is a reference to the building of the mill pool dam in 1465. There is a good view of the site from the railway viaduct over the Forder creek near Saltash. Wacker Mill and Dennybowl Mill were two other tidemills on creeks on the south side of the Lynher.

47 CARLYON HILL WINDMILL
SW 958754

There was a windmill on Carlyon Hill in at least 1690 and it may have worked intermittently until the early nineteenth century. The 30-foot tower is a landmark overlooking the Camel estuary. Three other windmill sites are known in the same St Minver parish.

48 COTEHELE MILL
SX 417682

+

The Cotehele estate mill worked until 1964. Its machinery and iron wheel have been restored by the National Trust and are displayed in working order. Outbuildings contain displays of craft tools used by smiths, carpenters, wheelwrights and saddlers.

49 HINGHAM MILL
SX 020725

The small watermill on the River Allen near Egloshayle is said to have been the last to work regularly in Cornwall, but is now derelict. It is unusual for its 16 feet 6 inches by 2 feet wooden undershot waterwheel, which worked two pairs of millstones. The machinery was made c1910 by G.H. Harris of Wadebridge.

50 LANDEWENDACK WINDMILL
SW 694152

The most southerly windmill in England. The tower may be the same 'Old Windmill'

marked on a map of 1695. It was repaired in the 1780s and a 'capital stone tower windmill' in working order was advertised for sale in 1828 along with a house, barn and a few acres of enclosed land. It seems to have closed around then and became derelict. The tower was used as a lookout in the Second World War. It is a landmark for miles across the bleak flat landscape of the Lizard peninsula, and it is also visible from the sea.

51 MAKER WINDMILL
SX 445529

There was a tower here at Empacombe in 1729. The site is unusually low, although the 25-foot tower stands on a knoll overlooking Millbrook Lake and the Hamoaze of the lower Tamar estuary.

52 POLTESCO MILL
SW 724157

The mill beside a narrow lane has an iron overshot wheel 17 feet by 2 feet, manufactured by Isaac Willey of Helston in 1901. Poltesco Mill became disused in the 1940s but has since been restored to working order. Two other corn mills in the valley are in ruins, as is the water-powered serpentine works (site 91) almost on the beach.

53 TREWERRY MILL
SW 838580

This was the nearest mill to Trerice manor, down in the valley below the house, and it has a datestone of 1630. It worked until 1950 but is now a private house. An iron waterwheel alongside was, manufactured by Jabez Buckingham of North Hill.

54 WAYSIDE FOLK MUSEUM
SW 454384

+

The fascinating Wayside Museum in the village of Zennor incorporates old mill machinery and millstones, while an iron waterwheel has been erected at the entrance. Lower down the same stream, there was a small corn mill almost on the cliff edge above Pendour Cove.

55 WEST LOOE TIDEMILL
SX 253537

The mill building is still recognisable, although now part of a boatyard. The large mill pool was used for many years as a boating lake but has now been mostly infilled for a car park.

Levant Mine

MINES

Metal mining is the industry most readily identified with Cornwall in the hundreds of roofless engine houses seen in the landscape from Botallack Mine perched on the Atlantic cliffs to Drakewalls Mine on the Tamar border at Gunnislake. The greatest mining field was around Camborne and Redruth, as well as at St Day, St Agnes, Pendeen, St Austell, Caradon Hill and Gunnislake, but many are the places where mining of some form has been tried in the past. The story of mining was one of hardship and became a struggle against falling prices due to increasing competition from foreign mines, ironically many of which were worked by Cornishmen. Copper mining reached its peak in the mid-nineteenth century before the industry collapsed after the 1860s, leading to widespread emigration of the mining population. Tin mining continued to the end of the twentieth century when South Crofty, the last tin mine, was closed. Other important minerals worked were lead, iron, zinc and wolfram, with many others including uranium.

The surface remains of a mine are usually more than just the tall buildings which contained beam engines for pumping, winding and stamping (ore crushing), for there might also be a count house (office), drying house, compressor house, magazine, calciner, carpenters shop, smithy, wheelpits and traces of round buddle pits where the crushed ores were separated. Another type of tin working was streaming, or the digging and washing of valley gravels to find and separate cassiterite or tin stone. This activity must date back to prehistoric times and most Cornish valleys and marshes have been turned over several times for their tin-bearing gravels. Deep openworks can be seen at Caradon Hill and Buttern Hill on Bodmin Moor, and other notable streamwork areas include the Red Moor and Pentewan valley around St Austell, Porkellis Moor near Helston, and the Carnon valley near Devoran.

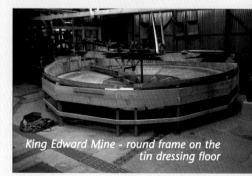

King Edward Mine - round frame on the tin dressing floor

56 BLUE HILLS TIN STREAMS
SW 729516
+
At Trevellas Coombe near St Agnes, a water-powered Cornish stamps and dressing plant produce small quantities of black tin for smelting on this site which is open to the public. The valley was once busy with stamps and dressing floors all the way down to the sea. Nearby, remains of the Blue Hills tin mine include a pumping engine house and the foundations of a horizontal engine which drove stamps and a winder.

57 CARADON & PHOENIX MINES
SX 265700 & SX 267720
South Caradon Mine (SX 265700) struck rich copper in 1836 and started a mining bonanza on Bodmin Moor, served by the Liskeard & Caradon Railway. The mine was worked eastwards from the Seaton valley far under Caradon Hill and extensive surface ruins include a cobbled ore floor, reservoirs, drying houses, tramways and pumping and winding engine houses. North of Caradon Hill is Minions, where an engine house on South Phoenix Mine (SX 261715) is now a heritage centre for the area. The Phoenix United Mine (SX 267720) worked for copper and tin in 1844-98, and had a dozen pumping, stamping and winding engines. The Prince of Wales Shaft (1907-14) had an 80-inch pumping engine built by Holman Brothers in an impressive engine house with a square-based chimney and tall brick stack. This complex includes buildings for boilers, a winding engine, compressor and stamps engine.

58 EAST POOL ENGINES & INDUSTRIAL DISCOVERY CENTRE
SW 674415 & SW 674419
+
East Pool tin mine has two fine beam engines preserved in their houses, both the property of the National Trust. A 30-inch winding or whim engine (SW 674415), with winding drum and flywheel, was built by Holman Brothers in 1887 and raised ores from Michell's Shaft at Pool until 1920. The much larger 90-inch pumping engine was installed at Taylor's Shaft (SW 674419) in 1924, having first been built in 1892 by Harveys of Hayle for Carn Brea Mine. Although East Pool closed in 1945, this engine was kept going to prevent South Crofty Mine from flooding until 1954 when electric pumps took over. Connected to this site, Cornwall's Industrial Discovery Centre in the old winding house provides an introduction to the county's industrial and social history.

59 EAST WHEAL ROSE
SW 839558
+
This rich silver and lead mine is famous for a disaster in 1846 when 38 miners were drowned by a freak cloudburst. During an attempt to revive the mine, a 100-inch pumping engine was set to work in 1884-5. It was widely travelled. Built by Harvey & Co. in 1853, it first went to Wheal Vor in Cornwall, then to a lead mine in North Wales before coming to East Wheal Rose. After the mine closed the engine went to

Phoenix United Mine

King Edward Mine - the tin dressing floor

an iron mine in Cumberland. The great engine house now stands in the leisure park of the Lappa Valley Steam Railway.

60 GEEVOR TIN MINE
SW 375345
+
The last tin mine in the Land's End district was worked by Geevor Tin Mines Ltd from 1911-86 and was abandoned in 1990. A tall steel headframe stands above Victory Shaft, below which are the tin dressing mills. The site is now the Geevor Tin Mine Museum. There are mining exhibits in the old buildings and guided tours around the twentieth-century surface workings and underground in part of an eighteenth-century mine. Beside the B3306 at Pendeen is the old timber headframe of Wethered Shaft (SW 378341).

61 KING EDWARD MINE
SW 664389
+
Part of the old South Condurrow Mine near Troon became the Camborne School of Mines' King Edward Mine in about 1904 and was used for training students. A museum here contains original equipment and rescued plant, including Californian stamps, a buddle, round frame, shaking table and reconstructed rag frame, which demonstrate ore processing in a clear

manner. One of the original wooden buildings contains a display of artefacts. The museum is alongside the Great Flat Lode Trail which passes through many important mine sites.

62 LEVANT MINE
SW 368345
+
Levant's workings ran out under the sea for over a mile. Originally a copper mine, tin was also produced after 1852. There was a disaster in 1919 when the man-engine collapsed, killing 31 miners and injuring many others. The mine closed in 1930. A 24-inch beam winding engine built in 1840 by Harveys of Hayle is preserved by the National Trust on the cliff edge and has been restored to steam working by volunteers of the Trevithick Society. The site also has the ruins of a pumping engine house, a compressor house for underground rock drills and traces of the man-engine house, with access leading to the shaft. Geevor Tin Mine and the dramatic ruins of Botallack Mine (SW 362336) are nearby.

63 POLDARK MINE
SW 683315
+
This tourist attraction at Wendron has underground visits through eighteenth-century mine workings. Outside displays of machinery include a 30-inch rotative beam engine of about 1850, which last worked at Greensplat china clay pit near St Austell from 1894 until 1959. It was the last to work in Cornwall and was moved here in the winter of 1972-73. Also displayed is a twin cylinder hoisting engine built by Holman Brothers in 1905. A museum tells of early tin working and the Cornish miner overseas.

64 TOLGUS TIN
SW 690443
+
The last of many small tin streamworks along this valley is found beside the Cornish Gold attraction near Redruth. Waterwheels work Cornish stamps and a dipper wheel, and other original equipment has been restored by the Trevithick Trust to demonstrate tin processing to the public.

The dangerous Cornish coast is protected by some of the finest lighthouses in Britain, including the Lizard which is unusual in having two towers. Other notable lighthouses are at Trevose, Godrevy, Pendeen Watch, the Longships and St Anthony Head, while the isolated rock towers of the Eddystone and Wolf can be seen far offshore on a clear day. Tater Du near Lamorna was added in 1965. Pierhead lighthouses are found, for example at Penzance, Newlyn and St Ives. Other navigational aids include daymarks, which range in size from the magnificent red and white striped Gribbin Head tower near Fowey to a small white daymark at Portreath. Signal stations, coastguard lookouts and houses are also part of the scene.

There are sufficient lifeboat stations around the notorious Cornish coast to deserve a mention here. The greatest rescue of all time was when 456 passengers and crew were taken off by Lizard lifeboats from the White Star liner *Suevic* aground on the Maenheere rocks in March 1907. The most exposed site is the old Lizard Point station in Polpeor Cove, where the first station was established in 1859, now seen with slipways and derelict houses of 1892 and 1914. Sennen Cove's lifeboat station and slip are also dramatic, while other stations such as St Ives have always relied on carriage-launched lifeboats. Examples of former lifeboat stations and slipways, no longer in service but sometimes put to other uses, can be seen at Coverack, Mevagissey, Newquay, Polkerris and Porthleven.

65 GRIBBIN HEAD DAYMARK
SX 098498
This red and white striped daymark was built by Trinity House in 1834 as a guide for shipping entering Fowey and St Austell Bay and to distinguish the headland from the entrance to Falmouth harbour. Square in plan, the tower is 84 feet high and partly ornamented at the top. The ruin of an Admiralty signal station dating from the 1790s lies nearby.

66 LIZARD POINT LIFEBOAT STATION
SW 701115
Very much a period piece, with two lifeboat houses of 1892 and 1914 at the very southernmost tip of the English coast, where the jagged offshore rocks can be much appreciated. The concrete buildings and long deepwater slipway in Polpeor Cove have been disused since 1961. The returning lifeboat was winched up a small slipway at the back of the cove, to be put back into the house ready for the next launch. There have been many lifeboat stations around the Lizard, at Coverack, Cadgwith and Church Cove.

67 LIZARD POINT LIGHTHOUSE
SW 704116
+
An early private lighthouse operated in

1619-23 but was opposed by Trinity House and local wreckers. The first lighthouse was built in 1752, with two octagonal towers supporting coal braziers forming an unreliable light. They were converted to Argand oil lamps in 1812 and then electricity when the Lizard had its own generator in 1878. Since 1903 only the east light has been used and it is now fully automated. This most southerly lighthouse in England is open to the public.

68 LLOYDS SIGNAL HOUSE
SW 715120
National Trust
This landmark on Bass Point was built in 1872 by G.C. Fox & Co. of Falmouth who

Lizard Point Lighthouse

Lloyds Signal House on Bass Point, Lizard
ALAN KITTRIDGE

used it with an overland electric telegraph to communicate between passing ships and their owners. Flag signals were used in the daytime and lamps at night. Lloyds took over in 1882 and carried on the service which lasted until 1951. The purpose was to identify ships passing into the English Channel and report to Lloyds and their owners and return any messages.

69 LONGSHIPS LIGHTHOUSE
SW 320253

A famous lighthouse marks the treacherous rocks around Land's End from which it is viewed by every visitor who comes here. The earliest lighthouse was seen in 1842 by Charles Dickens, who gave it a passing reference in his *Christmas Carol*. It is also the subject of J.F. Cobb's book *The Watchers on the Longships* (1876). It was a lonely position for the keepers, frustratingly close to the mainland and their cottages at Sennen. The 1795 lighthouse on Carn Bras was replaced by the present granite tower in 1873.

70 PENDEEN LIGHTHOUSE
SW 379359
+

Open to visitors, this lighthouse was erected on Pendeen Watch as late as 1900 along a dangerous coast between the lights of the Longships and Godrevy. Keepers' houses with flat roofs are part of the complex and these are now rented out as holiday cottages.

71 ST IVES PIER LIGHTHOUSES
SW 321406

Although John Smeaton's Pier was built in 1766-70, the old lighthouse near its end may not have been added until 1831. It was lit by gas from the new town gasworks. This low granite structure with a domed top became redundant when the pier was extended and a new white tower on the end was first lit on 29 September 1890. It was made of cast iron by Stothert & Pitt Ltd of Bath, a firm well-known for building dockside cranes. A similar lighthouse at Mevagissey (SX 018447) may be from the same makers.

72 TRINITY HOUSE DEPOT
SW 476300
+

From 1990 until 2004 Penzance was home to the Trinity House National Lighthouse Centre which contained a fascinating collection of lighthouse equipment. The centre was the former Trinity House depot which serviced the lighthouses and navigation buoys around the south-western coasts, when a lighthouse tender was based in Penzance harbour. It stands on the site of the workyard which was set up for preparing the stones for building the Wolf Rock Lighthouse in 1862-69.

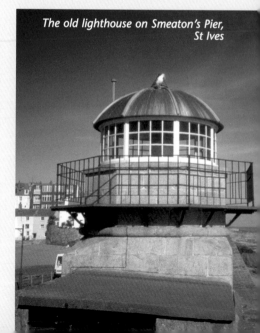

The old lighthouse on Smeaton's Pier, St Ives

PAPERMAKING

Paper was made in Cornwall from the early eighteenth century at small sites, often converted corn or fulling mills, but from the 1830s these paper mills were increasingly unable to compete from larger manufacturers elsewhere. An overshot waterwheel powered Danescombe paper mill at Calstock, where brown paper and board were manufactured from about 1788 until 1857 when the much larger Tamar Paper Mill at Hatches Green took over for 20 years. This mill had a 30 feet by 6 feet undershot waterwheel and became a bone crushing mill when paper-making ceased. The last paper mill in Cornwall was worked by Samuel Polkinhorne at Ponsanooth, before it stopped in about 1900. A wide waterwheel provided the power.

PORTS & SHIPPING PLACES

The estuaries of the south Cornish coast offer sheltered harbours which have served as trading or fishing ports for centuries. Even along the more rugged and exposed north coast many locations have seen some sort of landing or shipping place in the past. The fishing villages and their harbours are now very much part of the tourist scene but the trading ports are of more interest to the industrial archaeologist. Poor roads and the proximity to the sea meant that maritime trade around the coast was a vital lifeline, but trading was always limited in Cornwall because of its small population and isolation from the rest of England. The busiest ports were those serving the mineral trades, and today Fowey and Par still handle thousands of tons of china clay annually. The other exception is Falmouth where a ship repair yard with drydocks was established on a deep natural harbour and close to the shipping lanes of the Western Approaches. Falmouth had been a packet station from 1688 until 1852. Small trading boats took general cargoes to small quays as far up the estuaries as high tides allowed, and sailing barges were once a regular feature of the Tamar and all its branches. Even down to the 1970s, motor coasters still ventured up the Fal and Truro River to discharge their cargoes of coal, timber, cement and grain in the very heart of Truro. All this type of trade now goes by lorry. Padstow had a limited trade and small coal ships also came up the Camel estuary to Wadebridge until the 1960s. In the nineteenth century large quantities of granite were shipped from the De Lank Quarry's masonry yard on Wadebridge Quay, including the stones for the Eddystone Lighthouse in 1878-82.

The true industrial ports were those which served the mineral trades, and they may survive intact at the china clay port of Charlestown, or completely silted such as the copper-shipping quays at Devoran. Hayle, Looe, Newquay and Porthleven also owe their development to the mineral shipping trade. Features of interest around all these ports include quays, bollards, warehouses or crane sites. Most fishing ports also carried on a small commercial trade too.

73 CHARLESTOWN
SX 039515
The little dock and its outer piers were designed by John Smeaton and built in 1791-1801 for Charles Rashleigh, after whom the place is named. A lock gate allows shipping to stay afloat at all tides. Copper ore was first shipped but china clay became the mainstay in later years. The bulk clay was tipped down chutes on the east side of the dock, some brought through a tramway tunnel from the Carclaze clay dry. Period houses around the harbour, which is now used as a base for historic sailing ships, complete the scene.

74 COTEHELE QUAY SX 423680
Once an important landing and loading place on a bend of the River Tamar, with warehouses and limekilns. There is a small museum describing the trade here, while the restored Tamar sailing barge *Shamrock* can be viewed.

Pentewan

75 DEVORAN QUAYS
SW 798389

This busy mining port on the Restronguet Creek of the Fal estuary was served by the Redruth & Chasewater Railway which brought down thousands of tons of copper ore for shipment and returned with coal for the mine engines. The port is entirely silted up but some timbers remain of the upper quays, while there are granite bollards and the stone 'hutches' for storing copper ore on the lowest quay which has been restored as a public place. Point Quay (SW 800385) was also a shipping place on deeper water, and there were tin and lead smelting works here too. Older mineral quays on branches of the Fal, which were displaced once the railway was opened, included Roundwood Quay (SW 839404) and Pill Quay (SW 828384).

76 FALMOUTH DOCKS
SW 820325

The large ship-repair yard was founded in 1859, and foundries, engineering works, piers, heavy cranes and four drydocks followed. There is an excellent view over this active site from Castle Drive.

77 HAYLE
SW 562380 & SW 558373

Hayle shipped copper ores and imported coal, while also serving the town's two foundries. The Cornish Copper Co., who were smelting here, built a short ship canal and a dock in 1769 on the eastern arm of the estuary. The walls of the long narrow

Copperhouse Dock (SW 562380) have square slag blocks from the old smelting works, and granite walls with the remnants of lock gates survive at the dock entrance. The once-dredged channel of the 'canal' follows the south side of Copperhouse Pool. On the western side, a long quay in Penpol Creek was developed by Harvey & Co. for their foundry and trading businesses (SW 558373). Ore quays were built at the meeting of the two harbour arms and the entrance channel was sluiced clear of sand using water stored at Carnsew Pool and the Copperhouse Pool.

78 NEWQUAY
SW 808621

Newquay was developed after 1838 by Joseph Treffry for shipping iron ore and china clay, brought by a tramway which ran down into the harbour in an inclined tunnel. In the 1870s the Cornwall Minerals Railway connected Newquay to Par and built a wooden bridge onto the isolated stone pier which still survives in the harbour. The last trading ship called in 1922 and the harbour has returned to fishing and pleasure boats.

79 PENRYN
SW 789342

Penryn was a port long before Falmouth and warehouses can be seen at the head of the creek. Granite was exported in the nineteenth century and an iron crane by Williams & Son of Helston, 1864, survives on the old quay of the Freemans' granite works (now a boatyard). Above the bridge over Glasney Creek, the Anchor Warehouse belonged to the West of England Bone & Manure Co., bone crushers and manufacturers of sulphuric acid, dissolved bone, superphosphate and other artificial manures, and dealers in Peruvian guano. It is under conversion to living and office accommodation.

80 PENTEWAN
SX 019472
Sir Christopher Hawkins developed Pentewan for shipping ores and china clay after the Pentewan Railway was built from St Austell in 1829. Although a lock gate kept water in the dock, Pentewan had an ongoing battle to keep the entrance clear of the silt brought down by the 'White River' from the china clay district. Trade fell off after the railway closed in 1918 and the harbour basin became cut off by sand choking the long entrance between a pier and the cliffs.

81 PENZANCE
SW 477301
Much of the harbour behind the wall of Albert Pier (1853) has been infilled to make a car park, but Penzance's floating harbour of 1884 is the main interest. Tin ingots and china clay were once shipped from here, while general cargoes were also traded. Holman's dry dock and the Trinity House depot (now the National Lighthouse Centre, site 72) are also here. The South Pier's cast-iron lighthouse has a simple but solid design and was made in 1855 by the Copperhouse Foundry at Hayle. The lighthouse on Newlyn's South Pier (SW 468286) was made by Butler Brothers of Smethwick in 1914.

Copperhouse Dock at Hayle

82 PORTH NAVAS
SW 755276
Two quays shipped granite from the Constantine district. One is now used by a yacht club but there is public access to the other, with deeper water. It had a powerful crane and a squared granite block on the quay is a reminder of the former trade. The port is on a creek off the Helford River, at the highest navigable point of which is Gweek (SW 707266), a muddy place at low tide but where old wharves and warehouses tell of past shipping.

83 PORTREATH
SW 655454
A busy shipping place for the copper ores from the mines of Camborne and Redruth, there are two basins, built in 1805 and 1846, and a pier protecting the narrow entrance beneath steep cliffs. Although the south part has been redeveloped, the old harbour master's house remains and there are traces of ore storage hutches. Portreath was served by the Portreath Tramroad and a branch of the Hayle Railway which descended a long incline to the harbour. Coal continued to be imported long after the mines closed.

84 TREVAUNANCE PIER
SW 721517
It is hard to believe there was a pier at Trevaunance Cove before it was destroyed by storms in the early twentieth century, but the granite foundation blocks are revealed at low tide. It was built in 1794 for shipping ores from the St Agnes mines and imported coal was raised up the cliff by a horse-worked winding gear. Ore storage 'hutches' remain above the site of the pier.

Warehouses on Glasney Creek, Penryn

Cornish granite and slate have national reputations and their industries are still active in places today. For centuries, granite was cut from the 'moorstones' lying everywhere on the hills for local building, kerbs, paving stones, gateposts and many useful items. From the early nineteenth century high quality granite was quarried for major buildings and civil engineering works such as docks, bridges or lighthouses. Penryn became the greatest centre, with many local quarries supplying the Freemans' extensive workyard on the waterfront with blocks of granite for cutting, sawing and polishing before shipment. Large quarries on Bodmin Moor, at Cheesewring and around St Breward benefited from mineral railways to shipping places at Looe and Wadebridge, and quarries at Kit Hill and Gunnislake in east Cornwall and around Luxulyan near St Austell also relied on railways. Granite was shipped direct from Lamorna Cove, but most from West Penwith was carried by road to Penzance. The industry declined throughout the twentieth century with increased foreign competition and the introduction of mass concrete construction.

Delabole Quarry THORA KITTRIDGE

Some small quarries and masonry yards kept going mainly for local buildings or gravestones.

Today, the only major quarry is at De Lank, St Breward, where the latest technology is used in quarrying and stone dressing. This famous quarry has supplied quality granite for the Bishop Rock, Eddystone and Beachy Head lighthouses, many docks and countless projects in London and elsewhere down to the present day. On the other side of Bodmin Moor, though, Cheesewring Quarry is the most informative and is easily visited from Minions. Many stones on the moors show the marks of stone-cutting, mostly small lines of drill holes into which steel plugs were hammered between 'feathers' to split the stone. Examples can be found of the earlier method of chiselling out lines of grooves for inserting wedges.

Delabole is a name closely associated with Cornish slate and its quarry is the most famous in England. Hard grey Devonian slates of a high quality can be split for roofing, and slabs used for many other purposes such as tombstones, table tops, flooring slabs and lintels. In the district there were extensive slate quarries along

Cheesewring Quarry

the cliffs between Trebarwith and Tintagel, and further north towards Boscastle. St Neot was also noted for its slate which was sometimes worked underground such as at Carnglaze. Delabole and other quarries are still active, but on a much reduced scale due to competition from imports and other materials.

Roadstone quarries were opened in Cornwall from the late nineteenth century onwards wherever there were suitable hard stones, usually of igneous origin and often referred to as 'elvan'. The more interesting quarry sites were on the coast, so their crushed products could be shipped in sailing vessels, steamships and motor coasters to the south of England and northern European. The main areas have been around Porthoustock and Dean Point on the Lizard and Penlee (Gwavas) at Newlyn. Stepper Point near Padstow was important for a while, and numerous quarries around the Lynher estuary were served by barges taking their stone to Plymouth.

An unusual industry, but locally significant on the Lizard peninsula, is the working of serpentine. This attractive stone takes a polish and became popular in the Victorian period for ornaments and architectural work. Factories were established at Poltesco on the Lizard as well as at Penzance for this purpose, but have long since closed. Serpentine is relatively soft to work and can be turned on a lathe and polished so that today craftsmen make ornaments for the tourist trade around Lizard Point.

85 CARNGLAZE SLATE CAVERNS
SX 187668
+

The Caverns are underground slate workings where a quarry was worked back beneath the valleyside. They are on a much smaller scale than those in North Wales, but there is an impressive unsupported roof. Open quarries were the norm in Cornwall, although there were other small underground workings around St Neot and attempts at 'chambering' in the Trebarwith area of north Cornwall.

86 CHEESEWRING QUARRY
SX 258724
Cornwall's most impressive granite quarry, accessed through a rock cutting where rails of the old Liskeard & Caradon Railway survive. There are crane bases on the quarry floor and the main face has the marks of bore holes drilled for blasting. The vertical and horizontal joints show how large blocks could be obtained. Waste stone was trammed out onto huge tips, and the remains of workers' houses, a smithy and a powder magazine lie outside the quarry entrance. Around the moors there are abandoned stones destined for civil engineering works. Nearby is the flooded Gold Diggings Quarry (SX 249724), while to the north lie Bearah Tor Quarry (SX 259745) and the moorstones of Kilmar Tor (SX 249746), both once served by the Kilmar Railway.

87 DELABOLE QUARRY
SX 074837
The most famous slate quarry in England, once said to be the deepest too. Workings date back to Elizabethan times but the present pit has resulted from the amalgamation over many centuries of several smaller quarries. By the late nineteenth century the quarry was over 400 feet deep and the slate was hauled out by overhead cableways and a long incline with several tramways. The dressing yard was erected on the level top of a massive pile of waste. Here slate was split by hand or sawn and planed by steam-powered machinery. There is a viewing point and guided visits to the quarry and dressing sheds can be arranged.

88 KIT HILL QUARRY
SX 374717
This granite quarry lies within the Kit Hill Country Park. The workings are flooded but the old dressing area can been seen near the entrance. There are large waste tips and a long inclined plane took a tramway down to the East Cornwall Mineral Railway for sending stone to Calstock for shipment.

89 LAMORNA QUARRIES
SW 451243
Waste tips of large angular granite blocks stand out from the quarries on the east side of the valley leading down to Lamorna Cove from which stone was once shipped.

Poltesco serpentine works, Carleon Cove

The coarse granite was supplied for London buildings, the Longships and Wolf Lighthouses and the plinth of the Humphry Davy statue in Penzance.

90 PENLEE QUARRIES
SW 468278
In the early twentieth century the Penlee, or Gwavas, quarry was worked for roadstone by the Penlee & St Ives Stone Quarries Ltd. The roadstone was carried on a 2-foot gauge railway to Newlyn's South Pier, where there were facilities for loading coasters. A steam locomotive worked here until the 1940s, but the railway was replaced by a conveyor belt in 1972. The main Gwavas quarry, which produced an extremely hard aggregate, has now closed and left behind a massive scar between Newlyn and Mousehole.

91 POLTESCO SERPENTINE MILL
SW 727157
A factory for working serpentine was established by the Lizard Serpentine Co., partly in old fish cellars, at Carleon Cove in about 1860. Power came from a 27 feet by 4 feet waterwheel, to which a small steam engine was later added. Barges ferried finished architectural items to ships in the bay. The works closed in 1893 but there are still traces of the fallen chimney and sawn serpentine slabs. The walls of a warehouse (with 1866 date stone) have been conserved by the National Trust alongside an old capstan house near the shore. Along the cliffs towards Cadgwith is the old Signal Staff serpentine quarry (SW 726147).

92 PORTHOUSTOCK QUARRIES
SW 807218
The Porthoustock & St Keverne Stone Co. began quarrying northwards along the cliffs around Porthoustock Cove on the Lizard peninsula in about 1896, loading roadstone into ships from a purpose-built jetty. The quarries closed in the 1960s. The

Rosenython Quarry worked on the south side of the cove from 1906 until 1975, also using its own jetty. The beach here is partly formed from waste stone thrown into the sea. The last quarries are worked in gabbro at Dean Point further south (SW 803205).

93 PRINCE OF WALES QUARRY
SX 072863
A trail passes through waste dumps to an overgrown and flooded slate quarry in the Trebarwith valley. Features to note include the marks of blasting shot holes and one face which has been party worked in an underground chamber. Commanding the valley there is a prominent engine house and its chimney, preserved in 1976. Built in about 1870, it may have housed a beam engine to work an external winding drum connected to aerial ropeway cables which passed over a headframe (papote head) placed on a stone-walled 'strong point' at the quarry edge.

94 STEPPER POINT QUARRY
SW 915783
This roadstone quarry was worked in 'elvan' on the sheltered side of Stepper Point near the mouth of the Camel estuary, where ships could be loaded from a pier alongside. This is typical of many Cornish locations, where sea transport was essential to the existence of the quarry.

95 TREBARWITH CLIFF QUARRIES
SX 051872
Cliffside quarries can be viewed from the coastal footpath between Trebarwith Strand and Tintagel. Features include waste tips, and tall pinnacles left untouched by the quarrymen in Lanterdan Quarry. In places there are the round 'plats' of winding systems for raising stone from the quarries or lowering slates to small trading boats that came in under the cliffs to load.

Prince of Wales Quarry engine house

St Germans Viaduct

RAILWAYS

The first railways in Cornwall served the mining industry in the district around Camborne, Redruth and St Day. The horse-drawn Portreath Tram Road of 1812 had a terminus near Poldice Mine, from which copper ores were carried to the little port of Portreath. The 4-foot gauge Redruth & Chasewater Railway (1826-1915) ran from the copper mines of Redruth and St Day down to shipping quays at Devoran and Point. It displaced the packhorses which formerly served shipping places on other branches of the Fal, such as Roundwood Quay and Pill Quay. A coast-to-coast trail now follows the Portreath and Devoran routes. Portreath was also served by a branch of the Hayle Railway. Meanwhile, there were the Liskeard & Caradon Railway (1844-1917), Treffry tramways to Par and Newquay harbours and the East Cornwall Mineral Railway to Calstock Quay. The Bodmin & Wadebridge Railway was opened in 1834 as the first true steam railway in Cornwall.

The Hayle Railway (1837) became the West Cornwall Railway in 1846, opening from Penzance to Truro in 1852 and became part of the main line through the county shared with the Cornwall Railway which was completed in 1859 when Isambard Kingdom Brunel's Royal Albert Bridge at Saltash brought the railway across the Tamar from Devon. One of the great legacies of this broad-gauge line, engineered by Brunel, was the profusion of high timber 'fan' viaducts on stone piers crossing the many valleys of south Cornwall. All were eventually replaced with stone-arched viaducts alongside or occasionally rebuilt with girders on the heightened piers. The railways were later absorbed by the Great Western Railway and converted to standard gauge in 1892. There were branches to Looe, Bodmin, Fowey, Newquay, Falmouth, Helston and St Ives. There are several tunnels along the main line through Cornwall, but the longest was built in 1874 on the Cornwall Minerals Railway between St Blazey and Fowey. This Pinnock Tunnel (SX 105535) is 1,173 yards long and is now used by lorries taking china clay to the port of Fowey.

The London & South Western Railway's North Cornwall Railway entered Cornwall at Launceston and finally reached Padstow via Wadebridge in 1899. A branch starting in Devon was opened to Bude in 1898. The network was severely curtailed in the 1960s. Some original stations of the GWR and LSWR lines still survive throughout Cornwall. The courses of all disused lines are well worth exploring, although many sections are on private property.

Cornwall's only electric trams operated from 1902 on the Camborne & Redruth Tramway' carrying passengers between the two towns along a 3½-mile route which included a very steep hill at Tuckingmill. It closed in 1927, due to competition from motor buses, but a middle section continued to be used for hauling tin ores from East Pool Mine to stamps at Tolvaddon until 1934. Electricity was generated at Carn Brea until 1913 and the tramway depot at Pool was later taken over by SWEB.

96 BODMIN & WADEBRIDGE RAILWAY
SW 991723 to SX 086751

The original line of 1834 ran from Wadebridge to Wenford Bridge, with a branch to Bodmin. It was linked to the GWR at Bodmin Road (now Bodmin Parkway) in 1887 and this part has been preserved as a working steam railway, based at Bodmin General Station (SX 073664). The delightfully scenic course of the disused line through the Camel valley is now a footpath and cycleway.

97 CALSTOCK VIADUCT
SX 434686

Made of concrete blocks manufactured in the construction workyard on the Devon bank, this impressive viaduct was opened on 2 March 1908 after the East Cornwall Mineral Railway of 1872 from Kelly Bray to Calstock was relaid to standard gauge. The original line had descended an incline to Calstock Quay but it was now re-routed over the viaduct to give a direct link to Plymouth via Bere Alston.

98 CORNISH VIADUCTS
The stone or brick arched viaducts seen today replaced Brunel's original broad-gauge timber structures atop the stone piers which now stand alongside. In east

The picturesque Bodmin & Wadebridge line, now the Camel Trail

Cornwall, viaducts along the Cornwall Railway (later, GWR) start immediately after crossing the Royal Albert Bridge at Saltash (site 104). Notable examples include the St Germans viaduct (SX 364573), built in 1908 across the Tiddy branch of the Lynher and Moorswater viaduct (site 102) at Liskeard. Further west, large viaducts include Trenance (SX 010529) and Gover at St Austell, while the Truro and Carvedras viaducts spanning the Allen and Kenwyn valleys make a fine backdrop to the city of Truro. The former (SW 825453) is the longest in Cornwall, at 1,300 feet. There were eight viaducts along the Falmouth branch line, where the last to be rebuilt was Collegewood viaduct at Penryn in 1933-34 (SW 781342). The timber structures of some viaducts were replaced by building up the piers to support iron girders, all without interruption to traffic. Such girder viaducts are St Pinnock (SX 177646) and East Largin, rebuilt in the 1880s in the Glynn valley, Liskeard (150 feet high and rebuilt twice, in 1894 and 1929), and Coldrenick at Menheniot (SX 292611), dating from 1933.

99 LAUNCESTON STEAM RAILWAY
SX 329850
+

A narrow gauge railway follows the course of the LSWR west of Launceston station. Locomotives include historic steam engines of the late nineteenth century.

100 LISKEARD & CARADON RAILWAY
SX 237640 to SX 254748

Built to run by gravity, the sinuous course that carried granite and copper ore down from Caradon Hill to the canal at Moorswater fully opened in 1846. The middle route is lost in fields but on the moors it makes an excellent walk amongst the mine and quarry remains. One route encircles Caradon Hill while others lead to the Phoenix mines, Cheesewring Quarry and Kilmar Tor.

101 LITTLE PETHERICK BRIDGE
SW 921751
A three-spanned iron bridge across Little Petherick Creek was opened in 1899 to bring the North Cornwall Railway into the terminus at Padstow, 260 miles from Waterloo. The line closed in 1967 and its route is now a cycleway beside the Camel estuary from Wadebridge.

102 MOORSWATER VIADUCT
SX 237640
This magnificent slate and granite arched viaduct across the East Looe valley near Liskeard is 147 feet high. It was built in 1878-81 to replace Brunel's earlier stone and timber 'fan' viaduct, the piers of which remain alongside.

103 PENTEWAN RAILWAY
SX 011522 to SX 019471
The Westhill clay cellar (SX 011522) at the St Austell terminus of the Pentewan Railway remains in a car park. Parts of the route down the valley are visible but the harbour at Pentewan is the best survival.

104 ROYAL ALBERT BRIDGE
SX 434588
Brunel's masterpiece linking Devon with Cornwall across the River Tamar was opened by Prince Albert in May 1859. The Admiralty forbade the bridge to impede navigation and Brunel's solution was to design long viaducts from each shore to meet the two main spans of 455 feet (139m) which are part tubular and part suspension. Although since strengthened, the bridge largely survives in its original appearance.

Skew-arched bridge of the Liskeard & Caradon Railway

105 ST BLAZEY RAILWAY WORKSHOP
SX 074537
The Cornwall Minerals Railway locomotive depot (1872) was designed by Sir Morton Peto, who was a shareholder in the company. The turntable was outside and directed the locomotives to the 'roads' into the shed. The striking red brick building has been turned over to other industrial uses. The CMR linked Newquay and Fowey and was intended to carry iron ore for export.

106 TREFFRY VIADUCT
SX 056572
The Treffry viaduct was built across the Luxulyan valley in 1839-42 using massive squared blocks of locally quarried granite. This was the first major Cornish viaduct and included an aqueduct beneath the Treffry tramway, carrying water in a leat to work a large waterwheel at the Carmears Incline (SX 066567) before joining a second leat to Fowey Consols Mine and Ponts Mill. The wheelpit survives at the top of the incline which descends in a long curve to the valley floor.

Moorswater Viaduct

Pentewan Railway Clay Cellar, West Hill, St Austell

Packhorse bridge at St Thomas, Launceston

ROADS

The archaeology of roads in Cornwall includes many fine medieval bridges such as Greystone Bridge (1439), Horse Bridge (1437) and New Bridge (1520) on the lower Tamar, or Treverbyn Bridge (1412) and Respryn Bridge (1520) on the Fowey. Notable long bridges of the fifteenth century were at Looe and Wadebridge. The latter, 320 feet long with 17 arches, is said to have been built on foundations of wool sacks in about 1470. It was widened on both sides in 1847, and again in the twentieth century. Other bridges of interest include the 'clapper' bridges made of long slabs of granite found around St Breward on Bodmin Moor. This ancient technique was still used in the nineteenth century.

While important crossing points were secured by good bridges, the roads in between were generally said to be appalling during the winter months. No wonder that wheeled traffic was rarely seen until the eighteenth century. The problem was overcome by sea transport wherever possible, which was a convenient way to travel to and from London before the coming of the railways. Indeed, there was also a steam packet service between Hayle and Bristol. However, turnpike trusts were established in the eighteenth and nineteenth centuries to improve and maintain the roads which were carrying increasing traffic especially in the mining areas. The first was the Truro Trust of 1754 and at least ten others had been established by 1769 around centres including Bodmin, Callington, Helston, Launceston, Liskeard and Saltash. The Halworthy Trust linked Camelford, Wadebridge and St Columb in a northern route into Cornwall. The southern route, used by mail coaches between Plymouth and Falmouth (then a packet station), started at Torpoint where a ferry had been established over the Tamar. Two interesting late trusts of 1825 were a 2-mile route to Trebarwith, presumably related to the carriage of sea sand, or slate and a mile-long causeway at Hayle Bridge. The trusts were disbanded and transferred to the local authorities by the 1870s. Railways quickly took over the main routes but horse buses and vans continued to serve outlying villages. Bude's railway did not arrive until 1898 and horse coaches still operated from the Falcon Inn there for a few more years, perhaps their last outpost in England.

Far more miles of Cornish roads were left to the care of the parishes, but the legacy of the turnpikes can be seen in the alignments, cuttings and embankments of most main roads today, and more obviously in their toll houses and milestones. Direction stones and milestones are of special interest, but are often difficult to date. There are particularly fine granite stones carved with pointing hands in the Land's End area, some elaborate too, while another group is found in the parish of Stoke Climsland in east Cornwall. From the nineteenth century onwards, local foundries made cast-iron direction or finger posts, and some still survive around the county.

107 DELFORD CLAPPER BRIDGE
SX 114759
A late-nineteenth century version of the traditional 'clapper bridge' of large granite slabs carrying a moorland lane from St Breward to Blisland across the De Lank River. There are older clapper bridges upstream at Bradford (SX 119754) and Leaze (SX 132765). In the same area, Poleys Bridge (SX 083742) across the Camel is more elaborate affair with five slabby arches built in 1848 to replace an earlier bridge washed away in a great flood on 16 July 1847.

108 DUTSON TOLL HOUSE
SX 340858
A solid stone building of the Launceston Trust, on the A388 with two storeys and an extended porch.

109 HELLAND CROSS DIRECTION STONE
SX 091705
This and similar granite posts in the area around the edge of Bodmin Moor have squared caps with a destination carved on each face.

110 LAND'S END DIRECTION STONES
This district has a fine series of solid granite direction stones and milestones carved with destinations, distances and very descriptive pointing hands. The most elaborate stands by the A30 at a junction at Crows-an-wra (SW 395276), but there are different styles, for example at junctions on the same road at SW 376273 and SW 365262.

Direction stone, A394 near Helston

Pointing hand milestone at Crows-an-wra, A30 near Land's End

45

Westgate Street toll house, Launceston

111 LOOE BRIDGE
SX 254536
This long nine-arched bridge between East and West Looe was built in 1853 to replace a fifteenth-century structure. It was widened a century later but retains its overall appearance in slate with granite arches and coping stones. The very narrow bridge of 1436 stood about 100 yards downstream of the present bridge.

112 LOOE MILLS TOLL HOUSE
SX 232648
A handsome stone toll house of distinctive appearance, with a date stone of 1837. Now by-passed by the A38, it stands near Moorswater on the approach to Liskeard from St Austell and Bodmin.

113 MARAZION TOLL HOUSE
SW 523308
Toll house at the junction of Turnpike Hill and School Lane on the turnpike between Falmouth, Helston and Penzance. The central bay-fronted portion is two-storey, with single-storey wings. The stone post for the tollgate survives.

114 POLSON BRIDGE
SX 356849
This is an early bridging point of the Tamar at the county border. The historian Charles Henderson described the present bridge as a 'monstrous bridge of stone and iron' erected by 'mid-Victorian vandals.' It replaced a six-arched stone bridge standing on the site of one of the twelfth century, close to the early administrative centre of Launceston. Polson Bridge now carries a minor road, formerly the A30.

115 ST BREOCK TOLL HOUSE
SW 971726
One mile west of Wadebridge, near a junction on the north side of the re-aligned A39. An attractive toll house, still partly slate-hung and with Gothic windows.

116 ST THOMAS BRIDGE
SX 328851
A low packhorse bridge over the River Kensey close to the church of St Thomas at Launceston, with five low arches and cutwaters between. There are no parapets, and the more recent iron railings for the safety of pedestrians would now prevent the passage of laden packhorses.

117 TRESILLIAN TOLL HOUSE
SW 868465
A small single-storey toll house of the Truro Trust is beside the A390 in the village of Tresillian. It is in good order but has failed to find a new use.

118 WESTGATE TOLL HOUSE
SX 329844
A slate-hung toll house at a meeting of Western Road and Westgate Street in Launceston. The doorway is set to one side.

119 WOOD GATE TOLL HOUSE
SX 011529
A distinctive toll house in Pentewan stone, with Gothic windows, on the Bodmin Road (B3274) and almost beneath the Trenance railway viaduct at St Austell.

Marazion tollhouse

SMELTERS & ARSENIC WORKS

Tin ore was always smelted at home in Cornwall, at first in small charcoal-fired 'blowing houses' with furnace bellows worked by water power. By the eighteenth and nineteenth centuries larger smelting houses were established in most mining districts, using coal-fired reverberatory furnaces in which the fuel was kept separate from the ore, to produce 'white tin'. Notable tin smelting houses were Chyandour at Penzance, Mellanear at Hayle, and Calenick near Truro, a town which had Carvedras and two other works. Tin blocks awaiting shipment were once a common sight on the quays at Truro and Penzance. Uses of tin in the nineteenth century included bronze, solder, pewter and the tin plate industry, already established in South Wales. Other tin smelters were at Trereife (Newlyn), Treloweth (St Erth) and Point Quay. The last Cornish tin smelting works closed at Seleggan in 1931.

Copper was smelted at Hayle in 1758-1820 by the Cornish Copper Co. and the name Copperhouse still survives in the town. This was an attempt to break the Welsh smelters' monopoly in the industry, but it was always expensive because very large quantities of coal had to be shipped from South Wales to Cornwall for the smelting processes. In the end, a two-way shipping trade developed, with copper ores sent to the smelters on the coalfield at Swansea, Neath and Llanelli in one direction and coals brought back for the steam engines for the mines in the other.

There were lead smelting works at Point Quay and Par harbour. At the latter, the 'Par Stack' was a massively tall chimney until it was demolished in 1907 long after the works closed. Silver was refined from the lead at these works.

Arsenic was calcined at several mines to remove this impurity from the tin ores before smelting. A market was found for arsenic towards the end of the nineteenth century and larger works were built for calcining and refining arsenical ores. The chimney and flues of the 'lambreth' for collecting the arsenic soot at Botallack Mine (SW 364332) are well known and date from 1907, and a ruined works lies in the dramatic Kenidjack valley to the west (SW 360323). Near Redruth, there is a good example of a Brunton calciner, flue and chimney at Wheal Busy (SW 738445) and another calciner beside the B3300 in the Portreath valley (SW 690430). There were other arsenic works at Tolvaddon and Bissoe, with an important works at Gunnislake in east Cornwall.

Seleggan tin smelting works

47

Calciner in Portreath valley

120 CALENICK TIN SMELTING WORKS
SW 82143
The little hamlet of Calenick outside Truro was the site of the Calenick tin smelting works which operated in 1711-1891. The bell and clock tower remain.

121 COPPERHOUSE, HAYLE
SW 562380
The name is retained, although copper smelting ceased at Hayle in 1820. The chief physical evidence of this industry can be found in the dark blocks of copper slag (scoria) used in the walls of the Copperhouse Dock, the bridge across the head of the Copperhouse Pool, and walls and buildings in Hayle and Phillack. Some blocks were carried as far as Marazion.

122 GREENHILLS ARSENIC STACK
SX 418717
An enormous chimney stack dated 1894 marks the site of the Greenhills Arsenic Works on a hill above Gunnislake. Although damaged and once much taller, the stack is still a major landmark.

123 ROSEWORTHY ARSENIC WORKS
SW 606401
The English Arsenic Co. operated at Roseworthy from before 1873 until the Great War. A lone stack stands in a field above the site of the works, to which it was attached by a flue. It is visible from the A30 to the west of Camborne.

124 SELEGGAN TIN SMELTING WORKS
SW 695401
The Cornish Tin Smelting Co.'s works at Seleggan near Redruth was the last to close, in 1931. Some ruins survive beside the way-marked Great Flat Lode Trail.

TANNERIES

There were once many small tanyards throughout the county, although more were concentrated in the east. Leather was traditionally required for a multitude of uses, from boots and shoes to clothing, horse harnesses and tackle of all types. The tannin used in the process came from oak bark cropped from the wooded Cornish valleys or bark imported by sea. Eighteen tanners were still listed in 1897, including works at Launceston, Liskeard and Penryn but the last tannery in Cornwall was the Manor Tanyard of Josh Croggan & Son at Grampound.

TEXTILES

Cornwall had a small woollen textile industry, but nothing in comparison with counties further east. Late medieval fulling mills, were established, often at corn mill sites, for finishing woven textiles, and the place-name 'Tuckingmill' is indicative of their presence, for example at Camborne or Newport, Launceston. There was a carpet factory at Truro. A last woollen factory at Ponsanooth Mills survived until the early decades of the twentieth century. Here, the Cornish Smallware Co. Ltd. employed around 90 persons in 1897, manufacturing 'cotton tapes, stay bindings and all kinds of smallware.'

125 LAMELLION WOOL COMBING MILL
SX 239635
John Blamey's wool combing mill was beside Coombe Junction station of the Liskeard & Looe Railway. It was opened as the Duchy Tweed Mill downstream from Lamellion corn mill in the 1890s but the site has undergone major changes since.

THE WORKERS

Many Cornish villages and towns can be said to be industrial settlements, with their terraced miners' cottages. Mine captains and managers lived in more substantial houses. Such places include Camborne, Redruth, St Day or Chacewater, while Bugle and Nanpean are examples of clay-workers' villages in the St Austell district. Hayle is of special interest because slag blocks produced by the old copper smelting works are built into the walls of houses and harbour walls. Halsetown was established as a planned village in the 1830s by James Halse, MP for St Ives, with widely-spaced miners' houses built in pairs with gardens. There was a school and at one time there were three chapels too. The non-conformist chapel, sometimes more than one in a village, is characteristic of Cornish townscapes. Camborne and St Just have particularly fine examples of chapels. St Day, an attractive mining village with three streets forming a triangle, has the Holy Trinity church now roofless but preserved. Nearby, the famous Gwennap Pit is where John Wesley preached to miners and their families on many occasions.

Houses of individuals are of note, for example the thatched cottage at Penponds outside Camborne, once the home of Richard Trevithick, while in Cross Street, Redruth, is the house where William Murdock first used gas lighting in 1792. The Castle at Bude, (now council offices) was built by Sir Goldsworthy Gurney in 1830, where he invented the 'Bude Light'.

The Passmore Edwards Institute (1894) at Hayle

A review of industrial townscapes should also include institutes and libraries. Several were presented in the late nineteenth century by the Cornish philanthropist John Passmore Edwards, such as the libraries at Camborne, Liskeard, Redruth, St Ives and Truro, the Institute (1894) in Commercial Road, Hayle, or the St Agnes Mechanics and Miners Institute (1893). The Royal Cornwall Polytechnic in Church Street, Falmouth, was established by Robert Fox in the 1830s. It is now the Falmouth Arts Centre. Larger towns have market houses of the nineteenth century, such as Bodmin, St

Gwennap Pit

Austell or Helston. Workhouses at Falmouth (1852), Helston (1855), Launceston (1838), Madron (1838) and St Austell (1839) were substantial buildings, later becoming hospitals. Redruth has the Mining Exchange of 1880 in Alma Place, next door to the former Post Office & Savings Bank building of c1882, which is now The Cornwall Centre, an invaluable place for research into the county's past.

126 GWENNAP PIT
SW 717418
At Busveal near St Day, the pit where John Wesley preached was terraced all round as a memorial to the great evangelist after his death. It was originally a depression among old mine workings, an appropriate setting for one who preached to the Cornish miners.

127 MURDOCK HOUSE
SW 698420
The house in Cross Street, Redruth, was first lit with coal gas by William Murdock in 1792. He lived here in 1782-98 when he was erecting engines in the county for Boulton & Watt. It is now a community centre.

128 TREVITHICK'S COTTAGE
SW 637389
+
At Penponds, just west of Camborne, this thatched cottage was once the home of Cornish inventor Richard Trevithick. It was acquired by the Cornish Engines Preservation Society before coming to the National Trust.

Richard Trevithick's Cottage, Higher Penponds

129 ST DAY
SW 730425
This well-preserved mining village was once a market centre for the important Gwennap copper district. The population has declined since its heyday in the 1840s. Some houses are arranged around a triangle formed by Fore, Scorrier and Telegraph Streets, and there are good examples of early shopfronts. There is a clock tower and the unusual Holy Trinity church of 1828 has been conserved as a roofless ruin after 50 years of dereliction.